# Skills Practice
## Annotated Teacher's Edition

**Level 2**
**Book 1**

McGraw Hill SRA

*Columbus, OH*

**SRAonline.com**

 **SRA**

Send all inquiries to this address:
SRA/McGraw-Hill
4400 Easton Commons
Columbus, OH 43219-6188

ISBN: 978-0-07-610490-1
MHID: 0-07-610490-7


2 3 4 5 6 7 8 9 QPD 13 12 11 10 09 08

The *McGraw-Hill* Companies

## Unit 1 Kindness

### Lesson 1
**Phonics:**
/ā/ spelled *a, a_e* . . . . . . . . . . . . . . . . . 1
**Phonics:**
/ī/ spelled *i, i_e* . . . . . . . . . . . . . . . . . 3
**Selection Vocabulary** . . . . . . . . . . . . . . . 5
**Inquiry:**
Recording Information . . . . . . . . . . . . . . . 7
**Writing:**
Writing a List . . . . . . . . . . . . . . . . . . . . 9
**Spelling:**
/ā/ spelled *a, a_e* and /ī/ spelled *i, i_e* . . . . 11
**Study Skills:**
Alphabetical Order . . . . . . . . . . . . . . . . 13
**Grammar:**
Common and Proper Nouns . . . . . . . . . . . 15

### Lesson 2
**Phonics:**
/ō/ spelled *o, o_e* . . . . . . . . . . . . . . . . 17
**Phonics:**
/ū/ spelled *u, u_e* . . . . . . . . . . . . . . . . 19
**Selection Vocabulary** . . . . . . . . . . . . . . 21
**Inquiry:**
Recording Information . . . . . . . . . . . . . . 23
**Writing:**
Writing a Journal . . . . . . . . . . . . . . . . . 25
**Spelling:**
/ō/ spelled *o, o_e* and /ū/ spelled *u, u_e* . . . 27
**Grammar:**
Action Verbs . . . . . . . . . . . . . . . . . . . . 29

### Lesson 3
**Phonics:**
/ā/ spelled *a, a_e* and /ī/ spelled *i, i_e* . . . . 31
**Phonics:**
/ō/ spelled *o, o_e* and /ū/ spelled *u, u_e* . . . 33
**Selection Vocabulary** . . . . . . . . . . . . . . 35
**Comprehension:**
Sequence . . . . . . . . . . . . . . . . . . . . . . 37
**Writing:**
Writing a Fairy Tale . . . . . . . . . . . . . . . . 39

**Spelling:**
Review /ā/, /ī/, /ō/, and /ū/ . . . . . . . . . 41
**Study Skills:**
Following Directions . . . . . . . . . . . . . . . 43
**Grammar:**
Helping and Linking Verbs . . . . . . . . . . . 45

### Lesson 4
**Phonics:**
/ē/ spelled *e, e_e* . . . . . . . . . . . . . . . . 47
**Phonics:**
/ā/, /ī/, /ō/, /ū/ . . . . . . . . . . . . . . . . . . 49
**Selection Vocabulary** . . . . . . . . . . . . . . 51
**Comprehension:**
Reality and Fantasy . . . . . . . . . . . . . . . . 53
**Writing:**
Writing an Action Tale . . . . . . . . . . . . . . 55
**Spelling:**
/ē/ spelled *e, e_e* . . . . . . . . . . . . . . . . 57
**Study Skills:**
Using Newspapers and Magazines . . . . . . . 59
**Grammar:**
Subject and Predicate . . . . . . . . . . . . . . 61

### Lesson 5
**Phonics:**
/n/ spelled *kn_* and /r/ spelled *wr_* . . . . . . 63
**Phonics:**
/f/ spelled *ph* and /m/ spelled *_mb* . . . . . . 65
**Selection Vocabulary** . . . . . . . . . . . . . . 67
**Comprehension:**
Making Inferences . . . . . . . . . . . . . . . . . 69
**Writing:**
Writing a Personal Narrative . . . . . . . . . . . 71
**Spelling:**
/n/, /r/, /f/ . . . . . . . . . . . . . . . . . . . . . 73
**Study Skills:**
Using a Dictionary and Glossary . . . . . . . . . 75
**Grammar:**
Capitalization: First Word of a Sentence . . . . 77

# Unit 2 Let's Explore

## Lesson 1

**Phonics:**
/ē/ spelled ee, ea . . . . . . . . . . . . . . . . . 79

**Phonics:**
/ē/ spelled e, e_e . . . . . . . . . . . . . . . . . 81

**Selection Vocabulary** . . . . . . . . . . . . . . 83

**Comprehension:**
Author's Purpose . . . . . . . . . . . . . . . . . . 85

**Inquiry:**
Recording Observations . . . . . . . . . . . . . 87

**Writing:**
Writing a Descriptive Paragraph . . . . . . . . . 89

**Spelling:**
/ē/ spelled ee, ea, e, and e_e . . . . . . . . . 91

**Study Skills:**
Summarizing and Organizing Information . . . . 93

**Grammar:**
Complete and Incomplete Sentences . . . . . . 95

## Lesson 2

**Phonics:**
/ā/ spelled ai_, _ay . . . . . . . . . . . . . . . . . 97

**Phonics:**
/ā/ spelled a, a_e . . . . . . . . . . . . . . . . . 99

**Selection Vocabulary** . . . . . . . . . . . . . . 101

**Comprehension:**
Compare and Contrast . . . . . . . . . . . . . . 103

**Writing:**
Writing a Comparison . . . . . . . . . . . . . . . 105

**Spelling:**
/ā/ spelled ai_, _ay, a, and a_e . . . . . . . 107

**Study Skills:**
Using a Card Catalog . . . . . . . . . . . . . . . 109

**Grammar:**
Kinds of Sentences and End Marks . . . . . . 111

## Lesson 3

**Phonics:**
/ē/ spelled ee, ea, e, e_e . . . . . . . . . . . . 113

**Phonics:**
/ā/ spelled ai_, _ay, a, a_e . . . . . . . . . . 115

**Selection Vocabulary** . . . . . . . . . . . . . . 117

**Writing:**
Writing a Summary . . . . . . . . . . . . . . . . . 119

**Spelling:**
Review /ē/ and /ā/ . . . . . . . . . . . . . . . . . 121

**Study Skills:**
Table of Contents/Index . . . . . . . . . . . . . 123

**Grammar:**
Capitalization:
Proper Nouns, Titles, and Initials . . . . . . . 125

## Lesson 4

**Phonics:**
/ē/ spelled _ie_, _y, _ey . . . . . . . . . . . . . 127

**Phonics:**
/ē/ spelled ee, ea, e, e_e . . . . . . . . . . . . 129

**Selection Vocabulary** . . . . . . . . . . . . . . 131

**Comprehension:**
Author's Point of View . . . . . . . . . . . . . . 133

**Writing:**
Writing a Comparison . . . . . . . . . . . . . . . 135

**Spelling:**
/s/ spelled ce, ci_ and /j/ spelled ge, gi_ . . 137

**Grammar:**
Adjectives . . . . . . . . . . . . . . . . . . . . . . . 139

## Lesson 5

**Phonics:**
/s/ spelled ce, ci_, cy . . . . . . . . . . . . . . 141

**Phonics:**
/j/ spelled ge, gi_ . . . . . . . . . . . . . . . . . 143

**Selection Vocabulary** . . . . . . . . . . . . . . 145

**Comprehension:**
Classify and Categorize . . . . . . . . . . . . . 147

**Writing:**
Writing an Informative Report . . . . . . . . . . 149

**Spelling:**
Review /ē/, /s/, and /j/ . . . . . . . . . . . . . 151

**Grammar:**
Singular and Plural Nouns . . . . . . . . . . . . 153

# Unit 3 Around the Town

## Lesson 1

**Phonics:**
/ī/ spelled _igh, i, and i_e . . . . . . . . . . . . 155
**Phonics:**
/ī/ spelled _y and _ie . . . . . . . . . . . . . 157
**Selection Vocabulary** . . . . . . . . . . . . . . . . 159
**Writing:**
Timed Writing . . . . . . . . . . . . . . . . . . . . . 161
**Spelling:**
/ī/ spelled _igh, _y, _ie, i, and i_e . . . . . . . 163
**Grammar:**
Comparative Adjectives and Articles . . . . . . 165

## Lesson 2

**Phonics:**
/ō/ spelled _ow, oa_ . . . . . . . . . . . . . . . . 167
**Phonics:**
/ō/ spelled o, o_e . . . . . . . . . . . . . . . . . 169
**Selection Vocabulary** . . . . . . . . . . . . . . . 171
**Writing:**
Timed Writing . . . . . . . . . . . . . . . . . . . . . 173
**Spelling:**
/ō/ spelled _ow, oa_, o, and o_e . . . . . . . . 175
**Grammar:**
Capitalization:
Days, Months, Cities, and States . . . . . . . 177

## Lesson 3

**Phonics:**
/ī/ spelled _igh, _y, _ie, i, i_e . . . . . . . . . . 179
**Phonics:**
/ō/ spelled _ow, oa_, o, o_e . . . . . . . . . . 181
**Selection Vocabulary** . . . . . . . . . . . . . . . 183
**Comprehension:**
Fact and Opinion . . . . . . . . . . . . . . . . . . . 185
**Writing:**
Explaining a Process . . . . . . . . . . . . . . . . . 187

**Spelling:**
Review /ī/ and /ō/ . . . . . . . . . . . . . . . . . 189
**Grammar:**
Commas: Words in a Series . . . . . . . . . . . 191

## Lesson 4

**Phonics:**
/ū/ spelled _ew, _ue . . . . . . . . . . . . . . . 193
**Phonics:**
/ū/ spelled u, u_e . . . . . . . . . . . . . . . . . 195
**Selection Vocabulary** . . . . . . . . . . . . . . . 197
**Comprehension:**
Drawing Conclusions . . . . . . . . . . . . . . . . 199
**Writing:**
Writing a Summary . . . . . . . . . . . . . . . . . 201
**Spelling:**
/ū/ spelled _ew, _ue, u, and u_e . . . . . . . 203
**Grammar:**
Subject/Verb Agreement . . . . . . . . . . . . . 205

## Lesson 5

**Phonics:**
Open and Closed Syllables . . . . . . . . . . . 207
**Phonics:**
/ū/ spelled _ew, _ue, u, u_e . . . . . . . . . . 209
**Selection Vocabulary** . . . . . . . . . . . . . . . 211
**Writing:**
Writing a Persuasive Paragraph . . . . . . . . 213
**Spelling:**
Open and Closed Syllables; Review /ū/ . . . 215
**Study Skills:**
Parts of a Book . . . . . . . . . . . . . . . . . . . . 217
**Grammar:**
Contractions . . . . . . . . . . . . . . . . . . . . . . 219

## Proofreading Marks . . . . . . . . . . . . . 221

Name _____ Date _____

# /ā/ Sound and Spellings

**Focus**
- The /ā/ sound can be spelled with *a* and *a__e.*

**Practice** Read the following words. Underline the *a* or *a__e* spelling pattern used in each word.

1. b<u>a</u>sic

2. r<u>a</u>k<u>e</u>

3. f<u>a</u>d<u>e</u>

4. n<u>a</u>vy

5. c<u>a</u>n<u>e</u>

6. h<u>a</u>lo

7. <u>a</u>ble

8. b<u>a</u>sis

**Replace the underlined letter or letters with the given letter to create a rhyming word. The new word will have the same spelling for the /ā/ sound. Write the word on the line.**

1. <u>f</u> able    +    t    =    _____ table

2. <u>w</u> ave    +    g    =    _____ gave

3. <u>l</u> ace    +    f    =    _____ face

4. <u>m</u> ade    +    f    =    _____ fade

5. <u>c</u> able    +    st    =    _____ stable

 **Apply** Choose a word from the box below to complete each sentence. Write the word on the line.

| bacon | taste | bakes | trade | table | apron |
|-------|-------|-------|-------|-------|-------|

**1.** My favorite breakfast is eggs and _____bacon_____.

**2.** I will _____trade_____ you my apple for your banana.

**3.** Could you please set the _____table_____ for dinner?

**4.** Aunt Lucy _____bakes_____ the best cookies.

**5.** Dad wears mom's _____apron_____ when he is cooking.

**6.** Kathy can't wait to _____taste_____ the pie.

**Circle the correct spelling of each word.**

**1.**  baceon  (bacon)

**2.**  fak  (fake)

**3.**  daet  (date)

**4.**  laezy  (lazy)

**5.**  naem  (name)

**6.**  raek  (rake)

Name _____ Date _____

# /ī/ Sound and Spellings

**Focus** • The /ī/ sound can be spelled with *i* or *i__e*.

**Practice** Read the following words out loud. Underline the *i* or *i__e* spelling pattern used in each word.

**1.** i d o l

**2.** r i d e

**3.** i t e m

**4.** p i p e

**5.** s i d e

**6.** p i l o t

**7.** h i k e

**8.** i r i s

**Circle the words from above in the word search.**

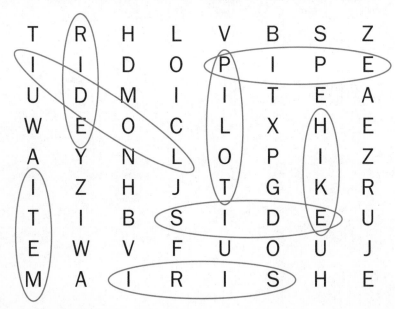

**Apply** Choose a word from the box below to complete each sentence. Write the word on the line.

| iron | time | dime | virus | kite | idea |
|------|------|------|-------|------|------|

**1.** What _____ time _____ does school start?

**2.** A _____ dime _____ is worth ten cents.

**3.** A _____ virus _____ is making Kate feel sick.

**4.** I love to fly a _____ kite _____ on windy days.

**5.** It was my _____ idea _____ to go to the park.

**6.** My mom still needs to _____ iron _____ my dress.

**Circle the correct spelling of each word.**

**1.** ida       (idea)

**2.** fier      (fire)

**3.** (wise)    wis

**4.** ireon     (iron)

**5.** (side)    sid

**6.** (rise)    ris

Name _____ Date _____

# Selection Vocabulary

**Focus**

**care** *v.* To look after.

**precious** *adj.* Loved and cherished.

**share** *v.* To divide into portions and give to others as well as oneself.

**feelings** *n.* Plural of **feeling:** an emotion, such as joy, fear, or sadness.

**kind** *adj.* Gentle, giving, and friendly.

**Practice**  **Draw a line to match each word on the left to its definition on the right.**

**1.** care

**2.** feelings

**3.** kind

**4.** precious

**5.** share

**a.** loved and cherished

**b.** to divide into portions and give to others as well as oneself

**c.** to look after

**d.** an emotion such as joy, fear, or sadness

**e.** gentle, generous, and friendly

**Write a sentence using one or more vocabulary words.**

I help take care of my dog.
_____

**Apply** **Use your understanding of the vocabulary words to complete the following activities.** Possible answers below.

**1.** Write about a time you were able to *share* something.

One time my friend was at my house and I was able to share some carrots at lunch.

**2.** List three examples of different *feelings*.

happy, mad, and sad

**3.** What is something that is *precious* to you?

my dog

**4.** Make a list of the people that take *care* of you?

mom, dad, grandparents, and teachers

**5.** Write one way you can be *kind* to someone else?

You can help someone if they are hurt.

Name _____ Date _____

# Recording Information

**Pay close attention to how people act toward each other every day. Record acts of kindness and courtesy that you see.**

Possible answers below.

| Where did it happen? | Why did it happen? | Kindness or Courtesy | How did the person react? |
|---|---|---|---|
| **1.** classroom | Andrew dropped some papers. | Sue helped Andrew pick up the papers he dropped. | He smiled and said, "Thanks." |
| **2.** playground | Zack and Joe both wanted to swing. | Zack let Joe go first. | Joe took turns too. |
| **3.** cafeteria | Mrs. Nelson bumped into me. | She said, "Excuse me." | I felt good. |
| **4.** home | My family was hungry. | Mom made us dinner. | We were happy and helped clean the kitchen. |
| **5.** store | The line at the store was long. | I let someone go in front of me in line. | She was surprised and told me I was nice. |

**How can you investigate kindness? You may have already started asking questions, such as what are examples of kindness. What else can you ask?** Possible answers below.

1. Why is kindness so important to people?

2. How does kindness help people?

3. What would happen if no one was kind or courteous?

**As you begin exploring kindness, keep a list of things you need to do. Check off each item as you finish it. Here is a start. Add to it as you read the unit.**

☐ Talk to friends about what being kind means.

☐ Talk to adults about kindness.

☐ Find and read books or stories about people or characters that show kindness.

**Name** _____ **Date** _____

# Writing a List

**Acts of kindness can happen anywhere. Brainstorm ideas for places where you could do specific things to show kindness.**
Possible answers below.

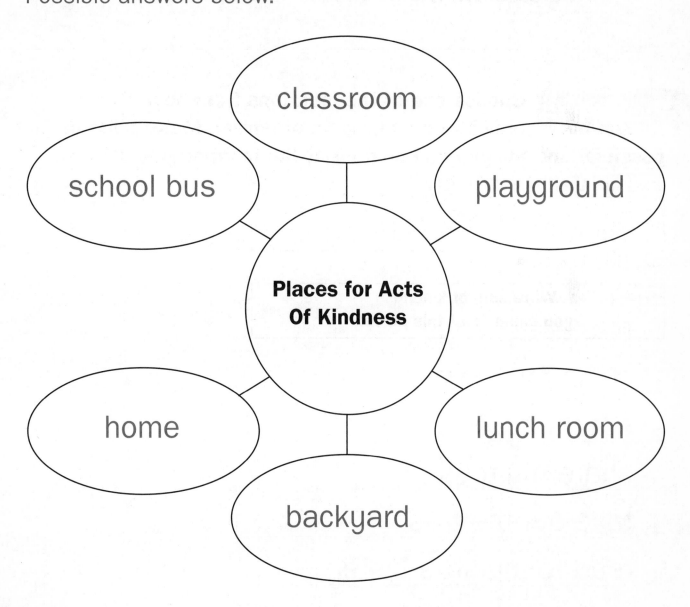

# Writing a List

 **Think**

**Audience: Who** will read your list?

_____

**Purpose: What** is your reason for writing a list?

_____

**Prewriting**

**Choose one of the locations from your brainstorming graphic organizer. Make a list of possible kind things you could do at the location you choose.**
Possible answers below.

| Title |
|---|
| Home |

| Write acts of kindness you could do at this place. |
|---|

1. clean my room _____

2. set the table _____

3. share my toys _____

4. take out the trash _____

5. read to my little sister _____

6. walk the dog _____

Name _____ Date _____

# Long Vowel a spelled *a* and *a_e*
# Long Vowel i spelled *i* and *i_e*

**Focus**
- Long vowels sound like their names.
- Two ways long *a* can be spelled are *a* and *a_e*.
- Two ways long *i* can be spelled are *i* and *i_e*.

**Word List**

1. mild
2. care
3. pilot
4. lady
5. bake
6. time
7. sale
8. ride
9. able
10. kind

**Challenge Words**

11. apron
12. final
13. quite
14. quiet
15. share

**Practice** Sort the spelling words under the correct heading.

long a spelled *a*

1. lady
2. able

long a spelled *a_e*

3. care
4. bake
5. sale

long i spelled *i*

6. mild
7. pilot
8. kind

long i spelled *i_e*

9. time
10. ride

**Apply** **Rhyming Strategy** Write the spelling word that rhymes with each set of words below. The new word should have the same spelling pattern.

1. stare    bare    care

2. rake    make    bake

3. side    hide    ride

4. cable    table    able

5. wild    child    mild

**Visualization Strategy** Circle the correct spelling for each spelling word. Write the correct spelling on the line.

1. (pilot)   pylet    pilot

2. lade    (lady)    lady

3. kinde   (kind)    kind

4. sael    (sale)    sale

5. (time)   tiem    time

Name _____ Date _____

# Alphabetical Order

**Focus**

- When words start with different letters, use the first letter of each word to put the words in alphabetical order.

- When words start with the same first letter, use the next letter that is different in each word to put the words in alphabetical order.

**Practice** Put these words from the story "Because of You" in alphabetical order. Write the words on the lines.

| can | of | and |
|-----|-----|-----|

and _____

can _____

of _____

Put these words from the story in alphabetical order.

| child | countries | care |
|-------|-----------|------|

care _____     child _____     countries _____

**Apply**   **Put these words from the story in alphabetical order. Write the words on the lines.**

| world | peace | teach | precious | kind | help |
|---|---|---|---|---|---|

1. help
2. kind
3. peace

4. precious
5. teach
6. world

**Write three words of your own. Then write them again in alphabetical order.** Possible answers below.

play

swing

friend

friend

play

swing

Name _____ Date _____

# Common and Proper Nouns

- A **common noun** names a person, place, thing, or idea. Common nouns do not begin with a capital letter.

Example
dancer, country, car, color, happiness

- A **proper noun** names a *certain* person, place, or thing. Proper nouns begin with a capital letter.

Example
Dr. Green, America, English

**Practice** Underline the proper nouns in each sentence.

**1.** Mrs. Smith has a new baby girl.

**2.** The baby's name is Allison.

**3.** We went to see the baby at Riverside Hospital.

**Underline the common nouns in each sentence.**

**1.** My class is reading about being kind.

**2.** We must do one kind thing every day.

**3.** Today, I helped Mrs. Jones find her glasses.

**Apply** Read the paragraph below. Underline with three lines the letters of proper nouns that need to be capitalized. Circle the common nouns.

My (name) is melissa. I am a (student) at goshen lane elementary school. Right now, I am in the second (grade) and mr. sanchez is my (teacher) My best (friend,) hillary, has a different (teacher) We get to play together at (recess) Every tuesday (afternoon) we have a music (class) together. (School) is a great (place) to learn new (things) and make great (friends)

**Read the common noun listed and write a proper noun to tell about yourself. Make sure to begin each proper noun with a capital letter.** Possible answers below.

| Common Noun | Proper Noun |
|---|---|
| **1.** name | 1. James |
| **2.** where you live | 2. Orlando, Florida |
| **3.** school | 3. Davis Elementary School |
| **4.** teacher | 4. Mrs. Brown |
| **5.** best friend | 5. Kenny |

**Name** _____  **Date** _____

# /ō/ Sound and Spellings

**Focus**
- The /ō/ sound can be spelled with *o* and *o__e*.

**Practice** Replace the beginning letter of each word with one of the following letters to make a new rhyming word. Write the new word on the line. Use each letter one time.

| j | d | r | w | m | s |
|---|---|---|---|---|---|

**1.** no _____so_____

**2.** nose _____rose_____

**3.** home _____dome_____

**4.** don't _____won't_____

**5.** host _____most_____

**6.** poke _____joke_____

Use the pairs of words above to complete the following sentences. Write the words on the lines.

**1.** Use your _____nose_____ to smell the _____rose_____.

**2.** _____Most_____ parties will have a _____host_____.

**3.** My mom said _____no_____, _____so_____ I can't go to the park.

**4.** The Eskimo's _____home_____ is in the shape of a _____dome_____.

**Apply** Read the word in the box. Then read the sentence. Change the word in the box to make a new rhyming word that will complete the sentence. Write the word on the line.

1. | cone | My dog loves to chew on his _bone_.

2. | toll | Mona put butter on the warm _roll_.

3. | fold | The man on the corner _sold_ hot dogs.

4. | role | We dug a _hole_ in the backyard.

5. | bolt | Suddenly, the train stopped with a _jolt_.

6. | nose | I watered the lawn with a _hose_.

**Circle the correct spelling of each word.**

1. (sold)          soled

2. oveal          (oval)

3. ow          (owe)

4. (hose)          hos

5. toen          (tone)

6. (old)          oled

**Name** _____ **Date** _____

# /ū/ Sound and Spellings

**Focus** • The /ū/ sound can be spelled with a *u* or *u__e*.

**Practice** **Read each sentence. Circle the word that correctly completes the sentence.**

**1.** Mr. Baker will _____ me in math.

    tuteor           (tutor)

**2.** Mom took some _____ pictures of the baby.

    (cute)           cut

**3.** Florida is one of the _____ States.

    Uneited           (United)

**4.** I _____ to give up.

    (refuse)           refus

**Circle the correct spelling of each word.**

**1.** (menu)           menue

**2.** musice           (music)

**3.** cubea           (cube)

**Apply**

| cute | humid | pupil | mule | huge | museum |

**Write a sentence using each word above.** Possible answers below.

1. This is a cute puppy.

2. It is a humid day.

3. We have a new pupil.

4. The mule pulled the cart.

5. The elephant is huge!

6. We went to the space museum today.

Name _____  Date _____

# Selection Vocabulary

**Focus**

**litter** *n.* Scattered paper and other materials; trash.

**witness** *v.* To see or hear something.

**dawn** *n.* The time each morning at which daylight first begins.

**engines** *n.* Plural of **engine**: a machine that uses energy to run other machines.

**glows** *v.* Shines.

**Practice**  **Write the vocabulary word that matches the definition below.**

1. <u>dawn</u>  the time each morning at which daylight first begins

2. <u>witness</u>  to see or hear something

3. <u>litter</u>  scattered paper and other material

4. <u>glows</u>  shines

5. <u>engines</u>  machines that use energy to run other machines

**Write a sentence that uses at least one vocabulary word.**
Possible answer below.
<u>We helped clean up the litter.</u>

**Apply** Make a poster to let people know that it is important to take care of our Earth. Use at least three vocabulary words on your poster.

Posters will vary.

**Name** _____    **Date** _____

# Recording Information

**Many people have jobs that allow them to show kindness while they are working. Use the chart below to record jobs people do that show kindness and how the people doing these jobs show kindness.** Possible answers below.

| Job | How does the person show kindness? |
|---|---|
| 1. teacher | 1. helps people learn |
| 2. nurse | 2. takes care of sick people |
| 3. police officer | 3. protects people |
| 4. fire fighter | 4. saves people from fire |
| 5. doctor | 5. helps people feel better |

# Summarizing and Organizing Information

Possible answers below.

**Write a topic related to kindness that you want to find out more about.**
How do people help the homeless?

**List some things you already know about your topic.**
Some people do not have homes.
There are places that can help homeless people.
Some places give clothes and food to people.

**What do you want to find out about your topic?**
What are different places people can go to get help if they are homeless?

**Find books, articles, or internet sites about your topic. Read them and write what you learn here. Use your own words.**

Inquiry • *Skills Practice 1*

# Writing a Journal

 **Think** **Audience: Who** will read your journal?

_____

**Purpose: What** is your reason for writing a journal?

_____

 **Prewriting** **Plan your entries. Write down what you will include in your journal.**

| |
|---|
| **Write the date of each entry.** |

| |
|---|
| **Write what happens to you or what matters to you.** |

**Write a list of possible journal topics. Have at least one topic about kindness. A few examples are given.** Possible answers below.

**1.** Write about something that made me happy yesterday.

**2.** Write about something that is important to me.

**3.** Write about playing with friends.

**4.** Write about a kind act I saw.

**5.** Write about what I did this weekend.

**Continue writing in your journal.**

**You can also include lists in your journal. Here are some kinds of lists you could write. Write your own ideas for more lists. Have at least one list about kindness.** Possible answers below.

**1.** Make a list of all the people I talked to yesterday.

**2.** Make a list of things I want to do on my birthday.

**3.** Make a list of my favorite books, television shows, or movies.

**4.** Make a list of my friends.

**5.** Make a list of the chores I do at home.

**6.** Make a list of kind things people do for me.

**What are some good reasons for keeping a journal?** Possible answer below.

remember things, write how I feel, think about special things

**How could a journal help you?** Possible answer below.

remember things, keep memories, organize information

Name _____ Date _____

# Long o spelled o and o_e
# Long u spelled u and u_e

**Focus**
- Long vowels sound like their names.
- Two ways long o can be spelled are o and o_e.
- Two ways long u can be spelled are u and u_e.

**Practice** **Sort the spelling words under the correct heading.**

long o spelled o

1. most
2. soda

long o spelled o_e

3. nose
4. joke
5. vote

long u spelled u

6. menu
7. unit

long u spelled u_e

8. cure
9. fuse
10. mule

**Word List**

1. menu
2. nose
3. most
4. cure
5. joke
6. unit
7. vote
8. fuse
9. soda
10. mule

**Challenge Words**

11. comb
12. bugle
13. total
14. human
15. suppose

 **Consonant-Substitution Strategy** Replace the underlined letter or letters to create a spelling word. The new word will have the same spelling for the long o sound.

1. <u>n</u>ote + v = vote

2. <u>h</u>ost + m = most

3. <u>ch</u>ose + n = nose

4. <u>br</u>oke + j = joke

**Visualization Strategy** Circle the correct spelling for each spelling word. Write the correct spelling on the line.

1. sodu (soda) _____soda_____

2. (menu) menyou _____menu_____

3. (mule) myool _____mule_____

4. kyure (cure) _____cure_____

5. phuse (fuse) _____fuse_____

6. (unit) younet _____unit_____

**Name** _____ **Date** _____

# Action Verbs

**Focus**
- An **action verb** tells what someone is doing.

Example

We **played** in the park for two hours.

**Practice** **Circle the action verb in each sentence.**

**1.** Every Saturday, I (play) at the park.

**2.** I (saw) some broken swings and litter.

**3.** My family (wanted) to help.

**4.** Mom and Dad (fixed) the swings.

**5.** Grandma and I (planted) some flowers.

**6.** Then, we all (cleaned) up the litter.

**7.** Everyone (said) the park was beautiful.

**8.** How can you (make) the world a better place?

 **Apply** **Read the paragraph below. Write an action verb from the box in each blank.**

| pack | use | recycle | help | love |
|------|-----|---------|------|------|
| made | save | sort | putting | take |

It is important for every person to ___recycle___. We can ___help___ Earth and ___save___ energy. You can ___sort___ trash at home into paper, plastic, and metal containers. New things can be ___made___ from these used items. People can also ___use___ things in different ways instead of ___putting___ them in the trash. For example, ___pack___ your lunch in a reusable bag. You can also ___take___ a cloth bag to the grocery store. There are many ways to ___love___ our Earth.

**Read the story below. Circle the best action verb for each sentence.**

The first Earth Day (**happened**) **are** in 1970. Every year on April 22nd, people (**do**) **find** things to **use** (**help**) the Earth. We should (**make**) **take** every day Earth Day.

Grammar • *Skills Practice 1*

Name _____ Date _____

# /ā/ and /ī/ Sound and Spelling

**Focus**
- The /ā/ sound can be spelled with *a* and *a__e*.
- The /ī/ sound can be spelled with *i* or *i__e*.

**Practice** Look back at "The Elves and the Shoemaker." Find one example of a word that uses each of the spelling patterns below. Write the word you find on the correct line. Possible answer below.

| *a* | *a__e* | *i* | *i__e* |
|---|---|---|---|
| table | make | kind | time |

Underline the spelling pattern in each word below. Draw a picture to illustrate each word.

**1.** pa_per   **2.** pla_n_e   **3.** spi_der   **4.** ki_t_e

**Apply**  **Read the word in the box. Then read the sentence. Change the word in the box to make a new rhyming word that will complete the sentence. Write the word on the line. Underline the spelling pattern in each word you write.**

1. | kind | I changed my ___m**i**nd___ about the party.

2. | crazy | Our ___l**a**zy___ cat sleeps all day.

3. | same | Would you like to play a ___g**a**me___ with me?

4. | size | I won first ___pr**i**ze___ in the contest.

5. | hike | Nelson does not ___l**i**ke___ ice cream.

6. | lady | It is ___sh**a**dy___ under the tree.

7. | grace | Please put everything back in its ___pl**a**ce___.

8. | mind | Did Alice ___f**i**nd___ her lost puppy?

**Write a sentence using a word with each spelling pattern given. Underline the spelling pattern in the word in each sentence.**

Possible answers below.

1. a ___The b**a**by was crying.___

2. a__e ___Will you er**a**se the chalkboard?___

3. i ___My best friend is from Ch**i**na.___

4. i__e ___Bees live in a h**i**ve.___

**Name** _____ **Date** _____

# /ō/ and /ū/ Sound and Spellings

**Focus**
- The /ō/ sound can be spelled with an *o* and *o__e*.
- The /ū/ sound can be spelled with a *u* and *u__e*.

**Practice** **Look back at "The Elves and the Shoemaker". Find one example of a word that uses each of the spelling patterns below. Write the word you find on the correct line.** Possible answers below.

| *o* | *u* |
|---|---|
| only | usual |

**Write a sentence using each word above.** Possible answers below.

1. This is the only hat I own.

2. Hot weather is usual in July.

**Apply** **Choose a word from the box below to complete each sentence. Write the word on the line.**

| perfume | music | rodeo | broke | excuse | pupil |

**1.** I said, "<u>Excuse</u> me," when I ran into her.

**2.** We saw horses, cowboys, and bulls at the <u>rodeo</u>.

**3.** Our <u>music</u> teacher taught us a new song.

**4.** Her <u>perfume</u> smelled like flowers.

**5.** When the vase fell on the floor, it <u>broke</u>.

**6.** Another name for a student is <u>pupil</u>.

**Read each hint. Fill in the vowel to complete the word.**

**1.** a musical instrument          b <u>u</u> gle

**2.** to give something away          d <u>o</u> nate

**3.** opposite of open          cl <u>o</u> se

**4.** musical tones          n <u>o</u> tes

**Name** _____ **Date** _____

# Selection Vocabulary

**Focus**
**leather** *n.* Material made from the skin of an animal.

**shoemaker** *n.* Someone who makes shoes.

**elves** *n.* Plural of **elf:** a type of a fairy.

**finest** *adj.* Nicest.

**flash** *n.* An instant.

**Practice** **Complete the following crossword puzzle.**

## ACROSS

**2** Material made from the skin of an animal

**3** Very nice

**4** An instant

**5** Type of fairies

## DOWN

**1** Someone who makes shoes

```
            ¹S
  ²L E A T H E R
            O
      ³F I N E S T
            M
      ⁴F L A S H
            K
      ⁵E L V E S
            R
```

**Apply**  **Circle the correct word that completes each sentence.**

1. My new shoes are made from _____.
   **a.** (leather)  **b.** usual  **c.** finest

2. There was a _____ of lightning during the storm.
   **a.** elves  **b.** (flash)  **c.** skipped

3. The _____ and his wife lived happily ever after.
   **a.** elves  **b.** (shoemaker)  **c.** midnight

4. Michael had the _____ pair of skates.
   **a.** leather  **b.** amazement  **c.** (finest)

5. _____ are in many fairy tales.
   **a.** (Elves)  **b.** Shoemakers  **c.** Customers

**Draw a picture of the following vocabulary words.**

**1.** *elves*     **2.** *shoemaker*     **3.** something that can *flash*     **4.** something made from *leather*

**Name** _____ **Date** _____

# Sequence

> **Focus**
> - **Sequence** is the order in which things happen in a story. The more you know about when things happen in a story, the better you can understand the story.
>
> - Some sequence clue words tell:
>
>   the **order** in which things happen: *first, then, finally*
>
>   the **time** or when things happen: *tonight, in the morning, once upon a time*

**Practice** **Look through "The Elves and the Shoemaker" for examples of sequence words.**

**1.** Circle the kind of sequence words the writer uses most often.

(time)       order

**2.** List two examples of sequence words or phrases from the story.

**a.** once upon a time          **b.** at midnight

**Underline the time and order words in each sentence.**

**1.** Tomorrow, my class will talk about our pets.

**2.** First, I will tell my pet's name.

 **Number the following events from the story in the sequence in which they happened.**

__3__ When he awoke, the shoemaker found a pair of shoes on the table.

__2__ One night, the shoemaker left his last piece of leather on a table.

__1__ Once upon a time, there lived a shoemaker and his wife.

__4__ For some time the shoemaker would leave leather and find shoes each morning.

__6__ At midnight, they saw two elves making the shoes.

__8__ When the elves found the clothes, they danced around.

__5__ One night, the shoemaker and his wife hid to see who was making the shoes.

__9__ Everyone lived happily ever after.

__7__ Afterwards, the wife made the elves clothes to keep them warm.

## Name _____ Date _____

# Writing a Fairy Tale

 **Audience: Who** will read your fairy tale?

_____

**Purpose: What** is your reason for writing a fairy tale?

_____

**Prewriting** Use this story map to plan your fairy tale.
Possible answers below.

| **Characters:** (people in the story) | **Setting:** (where the story happens) |
|---|---|
| Prince Louis and Princess Sophia | a big castle on a sunny spring afternoon |

### Plot (what happens)

| **Beginning:** (problem) | **Middle:** (events) | **Ending:** (how problem is solved) |
|---|---|---|
| Prince Louis and Princess Sophia are bored with playing games inside the castle. | They go outside to throw a ball back and forth. Prince Louis throws the ball out of Princess Sophia's reach. The ball makes a splash as it lands in a deep, dark well. | Up from the well hops a big, green frog. It is holding the ball. Prince Louis and Princess Sophia thank the frog. |

## Revising   Use this checklist to revise.

- ☐ Does your story have parts that make it a fairy tale?
- ☐ Are the setting, characters, and events imaginary?
- ☐ Is the problem solved with a happy ending?
- ☐ Do your words help the reader visualize what is happening?
- ☐ Did you use dialogue to make your story more interesting?

## Editing/Proofreading   Use this checklist to correct mistakes.

- ☐ Make sure to use proofreading symbols when editing.
- ☐ Is every word or special term spelled correctly?
- ☐ Did you capitalize characters' names, places, and the beginning of sentences?
- ☐ Does every sentence end with the correct punctuation mark?
- ☐ Is the dialogue written correctly with quotation marks?

## Publishing   Use this checklist to prepare for publication.

- ☐ Give your fairy tale a title. Remember to underline your title.
- ☐ Write or type a neat copy.
- ☐ Include a drawing of an important character or event from your fairy tale.

Name _____ Date _____

# Long vowel a spelled *a* and *a_e*
# Long vowel i spelled *i* and *i_e*
# Long vowel o spelled *o* and *o_e*
# Long vowel u spelled *u* and *u_e*

**Word List**
1. label
2. vine
3. bonus
4. wild
5. gate
6. huge
7. zero
8. made
9. spoke
10. use

**Challenge Words**
11. basic
12. program
13. usual
14. finest
15. caper

**Focus**
- Long vowels sound like their names.
- Long a can be spelled *a* and *a_e*.
- Long i can be spelled *i* and *i_e*.
- Long o can be spelled *o* and *o_e*.
- Long u can be spelled *u* and *u_e*.

**Practice** Sort a spelling word into each pattern:

long a spelled *a*

1. label

long a spelled *a_e*

2. gate

long o spelled *o*

3. bonus

long o spelled *o_e*

4. spoke

long i spelled *i_e*

5. vine

long u spelled *u_e*

6. huge

**Apply**  **Rhyming Strategy** Write the spelling word that rhymes with each set of words below. The new word should have the same spelling pattern for the long vowel sound.

1. mine    shine    vine _____

2. choke    broke    spoke _____

3. mate    rate    gate _____

4. shade    fade    made _____

5. child    mild    wild _____

**Proofreading Strategy** Circle the misspelled words. Rewrite the words correctly below.

You should always read the (laybel) when you are choosing a food item. It's good to (youz) foods that have (zeeroh) grams of fat. Choosing the right foods can be a (hyooj) (boanus) for your health.

1. label _____

2. use _____

3. zero _____

4. huge _____

5. bonus _____

Name _____ Date _____

# Following Directions

**Think of something you know how to do well. It may be a chore, a craft, or a game. Write the name of the task you do well here.** Possible answers below.

Make my bed
_____

**What are the steps for your task? Write the steps below.**
Possible answers below.

1. Pull sheet and blanket up to the top of bed.

2. Put pillow on bed.

3. Pull bedspread back.

4. Tuck bedspread under pillow.

_____

**Look over the steps. Are they in the correct order? Put numbers next to each step to show which is first, next, and so on.**

Now write each step clearly in the correct order. Use complete sentences. Draw a picture to go with each step.

1. First I pull my sheet and blanket up to the top of my bed.

Then I put my pillow on my bed.

3. Next I pull my bedspread up.

4. Finally I tuck my bedspread under my pillow.

Name _____ Date _____

# Helping and Linking Verbs

**Focus**

- Sometimes verbs don't show action. These verbs are called linking and helping verbs.

- A **linking verb** joins, or connects, the parts of a sentence to make it complete.

Example

> There **is** a pretty shell on the beach.

- A **helping verb** helps the main verb in a sentence tell when something will happen, has happened, or is happening.

Example

> We **are** planning to look for shells tomorrow.

**Practice** **Read each sentence. Write an *L* if the underlined verb is a linking verb. Write an *H* if the verb is a helping verb.**

**1.** I <u>was</u> swimming in the ocean today.      H

**2.** Fish <u>are</u> swimming in the ocean.      H

**3.** The fish <u>was</u> by our boat.      L

**4.** There <u>is</u> a fish in the pond.      L

 **Apply** — **Read the paragraph below. Underline the linking verbs. Circle the helping verbs.**

There are more than 20,000 types of fish. I (have) eaten swordfish and sardines. (Have) you ever eaten eel? A shark <u>is</u> a very big fish. <u>Are</u> sea horses fish? The lionfish <u>is</u> orange.

**Read the paragraph below. Write a linking or helping verb to complete each sentence.** Possible answer below.

There _____are_____ six fish in my aquarium. The blue fish _____is_____ swimming faster than the orange fish. My cat _____is_____ watching them swim. I _____have_____ tried to teach the cat to behave. These fish _____are_____ not for dinner, Miss Kitty!

**Name** _____ **Date** _____

# /ē/ Sounds and Spellings

**Focus** • The /ē/ sound can be spelled with e and e__e.

**Practice** Read each sentence. Circle the word with the /ē/ sound. Write e or e__e on the line for the spelling pattern of each word you circled.

**1.** (Maybe) Joe should go to the store alone.  ___e___

**2.** Did you (complete) the homework?  ___e___e___

**3.** Mom's birthday present is a (secret.)  ___e___

**Choose a word from the box that makes sense in the sentence. Write the word on the line.**

**1.** We ___began___ math class after lunch.

Mr. Jones showed us a problem.
___He___ helped us find the answer.

| |
|---|
| before |
| He |
| began |

**2.** Jessica is typing on the computer.

She wants to ___remove___ a word.

So, she presses the ___delete___ key.

| |
|---|
| delete |
| the |
| remove |

**Apply** **Look at the pairs of words below. Choose the word that will complete the sentence. Write the word on the line.**

1. Julia is sick and has a ___fever___.
   (fever, fevr)

2. An ___athlete___ is someone who plays sports.
   (athlet, athlete)

3. Let's ___pretend___ to be pirates.
   (preteend, pretend)

4. ___These___ books belong to Keith.
   (These, Thes)

5. The sidewalk is made from ___concrete___.
   (concret, concrete)

6. ___He___ is visiting us from Mexico.
   (Hee, He)

7. It is fun to watch teams ___compete___ in a basketball game.
   (compete, compet)

8. A sign in our yard says, "___Beware___ of Dog!"
   (Beweare, Beware)

9. Can you ___repeat___ what you just said?
   (repeeat, repeat)

10. You can make the toy car move using the ___remote___ control.
    (remeot, remote)

Name _____ Date _____

# /ā/, /ī/, /ō/, /ū/ Sounds and Spellings Review

**Focus**
- The /ā/ sound can be spelled with *a* and *a__e*.
- The /ī/ sound can be spelled with *i* and *i__e*.
- The /ō/ sound can be spelled with *o* and *o__e*.
- The /ū/ sound can be spelled with *u* and *u__e*.

**Practice** Use the words in the box to complete each sentence. Write the words on the line.

| brave | attitude | bride | overalls | music | find | table | robe |

1. We watched the _____bride_____ walk down the aisle.

2. Please put the dish on the _____table_____.

3. Keep a good _____attitude_____ when playing games.

4. The farmer wore _____overalls_____.

5. Did you _____find_____ your book?

6. Grandma always wears a red _____robe_____.

7. Kim tried to be _____brave_____ at the dentist.

8. Lucy danced to the _____music_____.

Unscramble the following words and write each new word on the line. Underline the spelling pattern in each word.

1. t    o    e    n          n<u>o</u>t<u>e</u>

2. z    i    e    s          s<u>i</u>z<u>e</u>

3. y    s    a    h    k     sh<u>a</u>ky

4. e    n    m    u          men<u>u</u>

5. l    a    o    t    t      t<u>o</u>tal

6. r    c    t    a    e      tr<u>a</u>c<u>e</u>

7. t    i    y    n          t<u>i</u>ny

8. u    e    a    s    m     am<u>u</u>s<u>e</u>

**Write the spelling pattern for the correct spelling on the line.**

1. Ohio    o            5. usual    u

2. huge    u__e         6. blame    a__e

3. hive    i__e         7. close    o__e

4. basic   a            8. tiny     i

**Name** _____ **Date** _____

# Selection Vocabulary

**snoozing** *v.* Taking a quick nap.

**raged** *v.* Past tense of **rage:** to act violently.

**furious** *adj.* Very angry.

**gnaw** *v.* To chew.

**repay** *v.* To pay or give back.

**Practice** **Replace the underlined phrase with the correct vocabulary word.**

**1.** My uncle was <u>taking a quick nap</u> on the couch.

snoozing

**2.** The hamster began to <u>chew</u> on the toy.

gnaw

**3.** I promised to <u>pay</u> her <u>back</u> for the snack.

repay

**4.** Stanley was <u>very angry</u> that his pictures were ripped.

furious

**5.** The lion began to <u>act violently</u> in his cage.

rage

**Apply** **Use your knowledge of the vocabulary words from this lesson to complete the following activities.**

**1.** Draw a picture of the character that was *snoozing* in the story.

picture of lion

**2.** What happened to make lion *furious*?

He was sleeping when mouse ran over his nose and woke him up.

**3.** Who *raged* in the story and why?

lion; Because he was caught in a net and couldn't get free.

**4.** How did mouse *repay* lion for letting him go?

He helped lion get free from the net.

**5.** How was the word *gnaw* used in the story?

Mouse gnawed the ropes of the net to set lion free.

**6.** Which two vocabulary words are similar? What makes them similar?

furious and raged; They both have to do with anger.

Selection Vocabulary • *Skills Practice 1*

**Name** _____ **Date** _____

# Reality and Fantasy

**Focus**
- **Reality** is people, animals, and objects that are in the real word. The events could happen in the real world.

Example
    My dog buried his bone in the yard.

- **Fantasy** is when animals, people, and objects do things they could not do in the real world. The events in the story could not happen in the real world.

Example
    My dog drew a map for his buried bone.

**Practice** Read each sentence below. Write an *R* if the sentence could really happen and an *F* if the sentence is a fantasy.

**1.** The library was closed today.      R

**2.** Our new teacher is an alien.      F

**Change the sentence above that is fantasy to a realistic sentence. Change the sentence above that is a realistic sentence to a fantasy sentence.** Possible answers below.

**1.** The library was flooded with tomato soup.

**2.** Our new teacher is Mrs. Jones.

**Apply** Look back at "The Lion and the Mouse". Write down the things in the story that are real and the things in the story that are fantasy. Write the examples in the correct box.

**Reality**

1. A lion and a mouse are real animals.

2. A lion is taking a nap.

3. The lion was hunting.

4. Lion was following a herd of zebra.

5. A hunter's trap caught lion.

**Fantasy**

1. The lion yells at mouse for waking him up.

2. Mouse promises to repay lion.

3. Mouse went to rescue lion from the net.

4. Mouse chewed the ropes to set lion free.

5. Mouse tells lion good-bye.

# Writing an Action Tale

**Think**  Audience: **Who** will read your action tale?

_____

Purpose: **What** is your reason for writing an action tale?

_____

**Prewriting**  **Use this story map to plan your action tale.**
Possible answers below.

| Characters:<br>(people in the story)<br>Fred and Jillian | Setting:<br>(where the story happens)<br>their house; a jungle |
|---|---|

**Plot (what happens)**

| Beginning:<br>(problem) | Middle:<br>(events) | Ending:<br>(how problem<br>is solved) |
|---|---|---|
| Fred and Jillian fall asleep while reading a book about the jungle and wake up in the jungle. They must find their way home. | They meet a baby elephant that takes them to its family. The elephant's family welcomes Fred and Jillian. Fred and Jillian spend the day with the elephants, but they still don't know how to get home. | Fred and Jillian fall asleep in the jungle and wake up at home. |

## Revising  Use this checklist to revise.

☐ Does your story have a lot of action?

☐ Are the setting, characters, and events exciting?

☐ Is the problem solved?

☐ Are the events in sequence?

☐ Did you use time and order words?

## Editing/Proofreading  Use this checklist to correct mistakes.

☐ Did you use descriptive words?

☐ Is every word or special term spelled correctly?

☐ Did you capitalize character names, places, and the beginning of sentences?

☐ Does every sentence end with the correct punctuation mark?

## Publishing  Use this checklist to prepare for publication.

☐ Give your action tale a title. Remember to underline your title.

☐ Write or type a neat copy.

☐ Include a drawing of the most exciting part of your action tale.

**Name** _____  **Date** _____

# Long e spelled e and e_e

**Focus**
- Long vowels sound like their names.
- Two ways long e can be spelled are e and e_e.

**Practice** **Sort the spelling words under the correct heading.**

long e spelled e

1. repay
2. beside
3. elect
4. pretend
5. hero
6. demand
7. meter

long e spelled e_e

8. eve
9. gene
10. these

**Word List**
1. repay
2. meter
3. eve
4. gene
5. beside
6. elect
7. pretend
8. these
9. hero
10. demand

**Challenge Words**
11. compete
12. create
13. evening
14. delete
15. eraser

**Apply** Visualization Strategy Circle the correct spelling for each spelling word. Write the correct spelling on the line.

11. uleckt (elect)    elect

12. (demand) dumand    demand

13. eeve (eve)    eve

14. (repay) reapay    repay

15. (pretend) preatend    pretend

**Proofreading Strategy** Circle the misspelled words. Rewrite the words correctly below.

What makes someone a (hearoh)? Is it a special (jeen) that they have? Is it someone who is really strong? No, (theaz) things do not matter. It could be someone who pays for your parking (meatur) when you are out of money, or someone who will sit (buside) you when you are hurt. Plain and simple, it is someone who helps you when you need it!

16. hero

17. gene

18. meter

19. beside

20. these

Name _____ Date _____

# Using Newspapers and Magazines

**Find a story or article in a newspaper or magazine. Then answer the questions below.** Possible answer below.

Is your article from a newspaper or magazine?

newspaper

Name and date of newspaper or magazine:

The Citizen Journal from May 10, 2007

Name of article and page it starts on:

Dog Saves Family From Burning House; It starts on page 2.

How many pages is the article?

The article is one page.

What is the article about?

The article is about a dog who barked to wake up a family because their house was on fire.

**Write a short summary of your newspaper or magazine article. Use complete sentences.**

Last night a house caught on fire. The family in the house was asleep. Their dog, Brutus, barked until the family woke up. The family was able to escape. Brutus was a hero!

Name _____ Date _____

# Subject and Predicate

- A sentence is a group of words that expresses a complete thought. A sentence has two parts: a naming part and a telling part.

- The **subject** of a sentence includes all the words in the naming part.

Example
The game of soccer

- The **predicate** includes all the words in the telling part.

Example
is played around the world.

**Practice** **Underline the subject once and underline the predicate twice in each sentence.**

**1.** Soccer began in England in the 1800s.

**2.** Two teams of 11 players each compete in soccer.

**3.** The players try to put a ball into the other team's goal.

**4.** The goals are two nets at opposite ends of a rectangular field.

**5.** Each goal is worth one point to the team that kicked the ball.

**Apply** Write an *S* if the underlined part is a subject, and write a *P* if it is a predicate. Put an *S* or *P* on the blank line after each sentence.

1. The game of rugby uses an oval shaped ball. _____ S

2. The players on a rugby team carry, kick, or pass the ball. _____ P

3. Fifteen players make up a team. _____ P

4. The object of the game is to score goals. _____ S

5. The team with the ball is the offensive team. _____ P

6. The game of football developed from the English game of rugby. _____ S

7. The team trying to stop the offensive team is the defensive team. _____ S

**Write three sentences. Underline the subject once and the predicate twice.** Possible answers below.

1. Joan and George like to play hide and seek.

2. Our class is getting ready for the craft show.

3. The girls are selling lemonade.

**Name** _____ **Date** _____

# /n/ Sounds and Spellings

**Focus**
- The /n/ sound can be spelled with *kn_*. When using *kn* together, the *k* is silent and you only hear the *n*.

**Practice** Add *kn* to the letters on the right to form a word. Write the word on the line and read it aloud.

**1.** *kn*      ee      __knee__

**2.** *kn*      it      __knit__

**3.** *kn*      ow      __know__

**4.** *kn*      ife      __knife__

**Apply** Choose a word from the box below to complete each sentence. Write the word on the line.

| knock | knight | knelt | knack | known |
|---|---|---|---|---|

**1.** The __knight__ is wearing a suit of armor.

**2.** Allison has a __knack__ for drawing.

**3.** You should have __known__ not to yell.

# /r/ Sound and Spelling

**Focus**
- The /r/ sound can be spelled with *wr_*. When using *wr* together, the *w* is silent and you only hear the *r*.

**Practice** **Write a rhyming word that begins with *wr* for each word given.**

**1.** song            wrong

**2.** note            wrote

**3.** list            wrist

**4.** map            wrap

**5.** neck            wreck

 **Apply** **Read each word or words. Write the word from above that you think of after reading the word or words.**

**1.** present            wrap

**2.** not right            wrong

**3.** hand and arm            wrist

**4.** tense of write            wrote

**5.** crash            wreck

Phonics • *Skills Practice 1*

Name _____  Date _____

# /f/ Sound and Spelling

• The /f/ sound can be spelled with *ph*.

 **Practice**   **Draw a picture of the word in the box.**

**1.** elephant

**2.** telephone

**Apply**   **Choose the word that best completes the sentence and write the word on the line.**

**1.** Grandma keeps a _____ photo _____ of me in her bedroom.
(foto, photo)

**2.** The _____ alphabet _____ has twenty-six letters.
(alfhabet, alphabet)

**3.** My best friend's name is _____ Ralph _____.
(Ralph, Ralfe)

**4.** Write a _____ paragraph _____ about kindness.
(paragraff, paragraph)

# /m/ Sound and Spelling

**Focus**
- The /m/ sound can be spelled with _mb. When using mb together, the b is silent and you only hear the m.

**Practice** Write the letters to the front of the mb spelling pattern to make a word. *Letters do not have to go in the order they are written.

**1.** a  l                      <u>la</u> mb

**2.** o  c                      <u>co</u> mb

**3.** l  i                      <u>li</u> mb

**4.** r  c  u                   <u>cru</u> mb

**5.** t  u  h                   <u>thu</u> mb

**Apply** Write a sentence with each word above.
Possible answers below.

**1.** We saw a lamb at the petting zoo.

**2.** Can you please comb my hair?

**3.** The tree limb fell to the ground.

**4.** I found a bread crumb on the table.

**5.** Lesley hurt her thumb yesterday.

Name _____ Date _____

# Selection Vocabulary

**Focus**

**escalator** *n.* Moving stairs.

**fastened** *v.* Past tense of **fasten:** to button.

**yanked** *v.* Past tense of **yank:** to pull.

**palace** *n.* A large, fancy house.

**dashing** *v.* Running suddenly.

**Practice**  Circle the vocabulary words in the word search.

```
F  W  T  I  V  N  E  S
A  A  E  S  C  P  M  W
L  P  S  R  O  M  Y  A
C  E  C  T  D  T  L  C
D  X  A  C  E  Q  V  P
P  T  L  D  H  N  A  O
A  I  A  N  M  P  E  M
L  G  T  U  F  U  E  D
A  I  O  O  L  J  I  Z
C  Z  R  B  H  Y  Y  K
E  M  R  E  P  Z  A  M
H  D  A  S  H  I  N  G
G  I  O  M  U  X  K  T
O  U  P  U  A  G  E  O
P  K  N  E  D  U  D  S
```

**Apply**   **Tell whether the boldfaced definition that is given for the underlined word in each sentence below makes sense. Circle Yes or No.**

**1.** The <u>palace</u> has thirty rooms.
   **a large fancy house** ............................................ ( Yes )   No

**2.** Paul <u>yanked</u> the thread on his shirt.
   **pulled** ............................................ ( Yes )   No

**3.** We rode the <u>escalator</u> up to the third floor.
   **a large fancy house** ............................................ Yes   ( No )

**4.** We saw the boy <u>dashing</u> toward the school bus.
   **being pleased with** ............................................ Yes   ( No )

**5.** Lisa <u>fastened</u> the overalls.
   **buttoned** ............................................ ( Yes )   No

**Write a sentence with each vocabulary word.**
Possible answers below.

1. I like to ride the escalator at the mall.

2. She yanked the button from my coat.

3. The dog was dashing across the yard.

4. Can you fasten this hook?

5. A princess lives in a palace.

Name _____ Date _____

# Making Inferences

 **Focus**
- Sometimes a writer gives us hints about an event in the story or about what a character is thinking or feeling. These hints can help readers make **inferences**.

- A reader makes an **inference** by using information from the story and information the reader knows from his or her experience.

**Practice** **Read page 100 of "Corduroy." Circle the sentence that is true.**

Corduroy hopes that a shopper will buy him.

Corduroy hopes that a shopper doesn't buy him.

**What clues let you know:**

Day after day he waited; the store was filled with shoppers, but

no one ever seemed to want a small bear.

**Apply** Write a paragraph about a game you like to play or a game you don't like to play without telling whether you like the game or not. Let your readers use the clues to figure out how you feel about the game. Possible answers below.

I play in a baseball game every weekend. I have been on a baseball team for the last three years. My team practices three nights a week and my dad helps me at home. Besides the practice time, my friends and I play games in our backyard. Sometimes, my mom and dad let me watch baseball games on the television.

**Read your paragraph to someone. Does the person think you like the game you wrote about?** yes

**Ask your partner for the best clue in your paragraph that told how you felt about the game. Write the clue below.**

I have been on a baseball team for the last three years.

Comprehension • *Skills Practice 1*

**Name** _____ **Date** _____

# Writing a Personal Narrative

 **Audience: Who** will read your story?

_____

**Purpose: What** is your reason for writing your story?

_____

**Prewriting** **In the left column, list a problem you have had. In the right column, list how you solved each problem.** Possible answers below.

| | |
|---|---|
| Before my piano recital I was nervous about making mistakes. | I practiced a lot, and I didn't make a mistake. Everyone was proud of me. |

**Use the graphic organizer below to plan your narrative.**

| | |
|---|---|
| **Problem:** | My piano recital was three weeks away, and I chose a difficult piece of music to play. |
| **Event 1:** | I practiced and practiced so I wouldn't make a mistake. |
| **Event 2:** | I was very nervous before the recital. |
| **Solution:** | I concentrated on playing my best. I played beautifully. |

## Revising Use this checklist to revise.

☐ Did you put events in the order that they took place?

☐ Do your ideas clearly show cause and effect of events that happen?

☐ Do you have a clear topic sentence?

☐ Did you correctly use time and order words?

☐ Does your interest or excitement show in the way you tell your story?

☐ Does your story have a beginning, middle, and end?

## Editing/Proofreading Use this checklist to correct mistakes.

☐ Is every paragraph indented?

☐ Is every word or special term spelled correctly?

☐ Does every sentence start with a capital letter and end with correct punctuation?

## Publishing Use this checklist to prepare for publication.

☐ Write or type a neat copy.

☐ Include a drawing, photographs, or a timeline to help tell about your writing.

**Name** _____  **Date** _____

# /n/ spelled *kn_*; /r/ spelled *wr_*; /f/ spelled *ph*

**Focus**
- One way the /n/ sound can be spelled is *kn_*. The letter *k* is silent.
- One way the /r/ sound can be spelled is *wr_*. The letter *w* is silent.
- One way the /f/ sound can be spelled is *ph*, as in the word *trophy*.

**Word List**

1. wren
2. knot
3. knife
4. write
5. phone
6. graph
7. wrap
8. wrist
9. phase
10. knit

**Challenge Words**

11. alphabet
12. wrinkle
13. known
14. nephew
15. photo

**Practice**  **Sort the spelling words under the correct heading.**

### /n/ spelled *kn_*

1. knot
2. knife
3. knit

### /f/ spelled *ph*

4. phone
5. graph
6. phase

### /r/ spelled *wr_*

7. wren
8. write
9. wrap
10. wrist

 **Apply**  **Meaning Strategy** Circle the correct spelling for each word. Write the correct spelling on the line.

1. Could you help me (rap, (wrap)) this gift? _wrap_

2. The string on my kite has a ((knot), not) in it. _knot_

3. Let's (right, (write)) a letter to Grandma this week. _write_

4. Have you read ((these), thes) books? _these_

**Visualization Strategy** Look at each word below. If the word is spelled correctly, write "correct" on the line. If the word is misspelled, write the correct spelling on the line.

1. nit _knit_

2. graph _correct_

3. knife _correct_

4. ren _wren_

5. fone _phone_

6. phase _correct_

**Name** _____ **Date** _____

# Using a Dictionary and Glossary

**Dictionaries** are books that include thousands of words and their meanings.

A **glossary** is a part of a book, usually at the end, that contains only words that are in that book.

## About Dictionaries and Glossaries

**1.** The words are in alphabetical order.

**2.** The words are spelled correctly.

**3.** Each word is defined or given a meaning.

**4.** Guide words tell the first and last words on a page.

Look up the following words from "Corduroy" in the glossary of your **Student Reader** and in a dictionary. Write the guide words from each source.

**1. sighed**

glossary: <u>sighed</u>       <u>still</u>

dictionary: _____       _____

**2. exclaimed**

glossary: <u>enemies</u>       <u>fee</u>

dictionary: _____       _____

Sometimes it is important to find a new word quickly in the dictionary. In your mind, divide the dictionary into three parts: a beginning, a middle, and an end. Words are found in different parts, depending on their first letter.

**Locator Chart**

A-F words     Beginning of the dictionary

G-Q words     Middle of the dictionary

R-Z words     End of the dictionary

In the space next to each word, write in which part of the dictionary the word can be found. Use the Locator Chart to help you. The first one is done for you.

1. amazing    beginning
2. enormous    beginning
3. wandered    end
4. gasped    middle
5. department    beginning
6. mountain    middle

7. mattress    middle
8. toppled    end
9. apartment    beginning
10. blinked    beginning
11. comfortable    beginning
12. sew    end

Name _____  Date _____

# Capitalization: First Word of a Sentence

**Focus**
- Capital letters are used in many places. One place capital letters are used is at the beginning of a sentence.

- A sentence always begins with a capital letter.
Example
  **C**amping is fun. **H**ave you ever slept outside?

**Practice**  **Underline the beginning letter of each sentence three times.**

did you know that the teddy bear is over one hundred years

old? this popular toy has been around longer than the electric

light, telephone, and motor car. in 1902, President Theodore

Roosevelt was on a hunting trip and had the chance to shoot a

captured bear. he refused, saying "Spare the bear!" a cartoon

was drawn of this event and was put into the newspaper.

two shopkeepers, Morris and Rose Michtom, made a soft bear

that they called Teddy's Bear. the teddy bear was an overnight

success and still very popular today.

**Apply** **Write a paragraph about your most special toy. After writing, go back and circle the first letter of each sentence. Make sure it is a capital letter.** Possible answers below.

Ⓦhen I was five years old I was given a stuffed dog as a present. Ⓘt was a white dog with black spots and I named her Freckles. Ⓕreckles went everywhere with me and we had so much fun together. Ⓔvery night, Freckles would sleep with me. Ⓝow that I am bigger, I still have Freckles and I keep her safe in my room. Ⓦe don't seem to play together as much, but she will always be my most special toy.

**Underline three times the letters that should be capital letters.**

Dear Corduroy,

i think you are a very nice bear. lisa is very lucky to have

you as her special friend. i bet you like living with Lisa. she takes

good care of you. it was nice of her to fix your overalls. she also

had your own bed ready and waiting for you. make sure to be a

good friend to her as well.

Sincerely,

A Corduroy Fan

Name _____ Date _____

# /ē/ Sound and Spellings

**Focus** • The /ē/ sound can be spelled with *ee* and *ea*.

**Practice** Read the following words aloud.

| | | | |
|---|---|---|---|
| dream | green | cheat | pea |
| feet | keep | leak | peek |

**Write the words with the /ē/ sound spelled like *leaf*.**

1. dream
2. cheat
3. pea
4. leak

**Write the words with the /ē/ sound spelled like *weed*.**

1. green
2. feet
3. keep
4. peek

**Apply** Read the word in the box. Then read the sentence. Change the word in the box to make a new rhyming word to complete the sentence.

1. | hear | If it is ___clear___ you can see through it.

2. | tree | If you don't have to pay, then it is ___free___.

3. | reach | If you want to find seashells, go to the ___beach___.

4. | beep | If you're not giving it away, it's yours to ___keep___.

5. | beam | If you are an athlete, you might be on a ___team___.

6. | week | If you are spying, you might sneak a ___peek___.

7. | weed | If you want a flower to grow, you should plant a ___seed___.

8. | peach | If something is up high, you'll have to ___reach___ for it.

Phonics • *Skills Practice 1*

Name _____ Date _____

# /ē/ Sounds and Spellings

**Focus** • The /ē/ sound can be spelled with e and e_e.

**Practice** **Read the words in the box. Choose the correct word to complete each sentence.**

| equal | eve | theme | eleven | stampede | begin |
|-------|-----|-------|--------|----------|-------|

1. There was a ___stampede___ of running horses.

2. Everyone gets an ___equal___ share of the prize.

3. Andrea will be ___eleven___ years old.

4. "Let's Explore" is the ___theme___ of this unit.

5. The night before a special day is called the ___eve___.

6. Should I ___begin___ reading?

**Apply** Read each sentence. Circle the word that correctly completes the sentence.

1. Kendra reads a story every _____.
   a. (evening)   b. eevenin   c. eavening

2. Did you _____ the homework?
   a. complet   b. compleet   c. (complete)

3. Shawn will _____ in the spelling bee.
   a. compeet   b. (compete)   c. compeate

4. _____ comes before the number one.
   a. (Zero)   b. Zeeroe   c. Zereo

5. I will _____ to her letter soon.
   a. reaply   b. repely   c. (reply)

6. _____ is my best friend.
   a. (Steve)   b. Steevee   c. Steave

7. Can you _____ what you said?
   a. reapeat   b. (repeat)   c. repet

8. Just take a deep breath and _____.
   a. (relax)   b. realax   c. releax

Phonics • *Skills Practice 1*

Name _____  Date _____

## Selection Vocabulary

**Focus**

**insects** *n.* Plural of **insect**: a six-legged bug.

**invade** *v.* To enter without an invitation.

**cocoon** *n.* A case that protects an insect while it changes to an adult.

**tunnels** *n.* Plural of **tunnel**: an underground passageway.

**enemies** *n.* Plural of **enemy**: a person or thing that wants to hurt another.

**Practice**  Complete the crossword puzzle.

|   |   |   |   |   |   |
|---|---|---|---|---|---|
| ¹i | n | s | e | c | ²t |
|   |   |   |   |   | u |
| ³c | o | c | o | o | n |
|   |   |   |   |   | n |
| ⁴i | n | v | a | d | e |
|   |   |   |   |   | l |
| ⁵e | n | e | m | i | e | s |

**Across**

**1.** A six-legged bug

**3.** A case that protects an insect while it changes

**4.** To enter without an invitation

**5.** People or things that want to hurt another

**Down**

**2.** Underground passageways

**Apply** **Complete each sentence with a vocabulary word and then answer the question.** Possible answers below.

| insects | cocoon | enemies | invade | tunnels |
|---------|--------|---------|--------|---------|

**1.** All _____insects_____ have six legs and three body parts.

*What is an example of an insect?* _____ant_____

**2.** Ants must protect themselves from _____enemies_____.

*What is an enemy of an ant?* _____a spider_____

**3.** The underground passages are called _____tunnels_____.

*Why do ants dig tunnels?* _____
They are part of their nest._____

**4.** A pupa ant grows inside a _____cocoon_____.

*What is another animal that grows inside of a cocoon?*
_____butterfly_____

**5.** Look out! Ants are going to _____invade_____ the picnic!

*Why do you think ants would invade your picnic?*
_____to get food_____

**Name** _____ **Date** _____

# Author's Purpose

> **Focus**
> - Author's write for different reasons. Sometimes they want to give readers information. Sometimes they write to entertain.
>
> - Writers *entertain* readers by including
>   - funny words or events
>   - exciting or familiar events
> - Writers *inform* readers by including
>   - facts that can be proven
> - Writers *persuade* readers by including
>   - their opinions

**Practice** Numbered below are some titles of stories. A list of purposes that authors can use is in the box. Choose the one that fits each title.

| entertain | inform | persuade |
| --- | --- | --- |

**1.** "Why the School Year Should Be Longer"

   persuade

**2.** "The Great Mahooleywhazit and the Big YUCK!"

   entertain

**3.** "Ocean Animals"

   inform

**Apply** Answer the following questions.

What is the author's purpose of "Ants! They are hard workers!"?

inform

Write a reason for your answer.

There are facts written that can be proven.

Name _____ Date _____

# Recording Observations

After going on your nature walk, think about the different things that you observed. Write down these things under the correct category: *Living Things* or *Nonliving Things*. Possible answers below.

***Living Things***

1. spider
2. tree
3. dog
4. people
5. flower

***Nonliving Things***

1. birdhouse
2. house
3. swingset
4. school
5. bus

**How can you tell if something is living or nonliving?**
It can grow.
**Look around the classroom. Write examples of three living and three nonliving things.** Possible answers below.

*Living Things*

1. teacher
2. students
3. plants

*Nonliving Things*

1. pencil
2. desks
3. books

　　　　　　　Inquiry • *Skills Practice 1*

# Writing a Descriptive Paragraph

 **Audience: Who** will read your paragraph?

_____

**Purpose: What** is your reason for writing your paragraph?

_____

**Prewriting** **Your answers below will help you write your description.** Possible answers below.

**1. What did you see?**

blue skies, waves, sun, seagulls
_____

**2. What did you feel to the touch?**

warm sand, cool water
_____

**3. What did you smell?**

fresh air, saltwater
_____

**4. What did you hear?**

crashing waves, wind blowing
_____

**5. What did you taste?**

saltwater
_____

## Revising — Use this checklist to revise.

- ☐ Do you have a clear topic sentence?
- ☐ Do your other sentences support the topic sentence?
- ☐ Do the words you use give a good description?
- ☐ Could you change any words to be more descriptive?
- ☐ Is there anything else you want to add to your paragraph?

## Editing/Proofreading — Use this checklist to correct mistakes.

- ☐ Is the paragraph indented?
- ☐ Make sure all of your sentences are complete.
- ☐ Is every word or special term spelled correctly?
- ☐ Does every sentence start with a capital letter and end with correct punctuation?

## Publishing — Use this checklist to prepare for publication.

- ☐ Write or type a neat copy.
- ☐ Include a drawing of your topic.

**UNIT 2** Lesson 1

**Name** _____  **Date** _____

# Long e spelled ee, ea, e, e_e

**Focus** The long e sound can be spelled many ways. Some of the ways it can be spelled are: ee, ea, e, and e_e.

**Practice** **Sort the spelling words under the correct heading.**

**Long e spelled ee**

1. sleep
2. feel
3. green
4. knee

**Long e spelled ea**

5. real
6. east
7. team
8. clear

**Long e spelled e**

9. we
10. belong

**Word List**

1. real
2. sleep
3. we
4. feel
5. east
6. green
7. team
8. belong
9. knee
10. clear

**Challenge Words**

11. peach
12. cheese
13. please
14. between
15. eagle

**Apply** Pronunciation Strategy Underline the letters that spell the long e sound in each word as you pronounce them. Then, write a spelling word with the same spelling of the long e sound as each set of words below.

Possible answers below.

1. beat    steam    real
2. reed    sheep    green
3. me    become    belong
4. bee    steel    knee
5. fear · meal    clear

Visualization Strategy Circle the correct spelling for each word. Then write the correct spelling on the line.

1. slepe    (sleep)    sleep
2. (team)    teme    team
3. (feel)    feal    feel
4. wea    (we)    we
5. eeste    (east)    east

Name _____ Date _____

# Summarizing and Organizing Information

**Focus**
- Writing a **summary** helps you organize the information from a piece of writing.
- A **summary** tells the *main idea* and *main points* of a longer piece of writing.

**Practice** **Write a topic related to the natural world that you want to find out more about.**

Possible answers below.

**List some things you already know about your topic.**

dolphins live in the ocean, they live in groups, they can communicate

**Who:** Who knows a lot about dolphins?

**What:** What do dolphins 'say' to each other?

**When:** When do they 'talk' to each other?

**Where:** Where can you find dolphins?

**Why:** Why do dolphins 'talk'?

**How:** How do dolphins understand each other?

**Apply** **Find books or magazines about your topic. Read them and write what you learn here. Use your own words.**

Possible answers below.

**Who:** Marine biologists know a lot about dolphins.

**What:** Dolphins tell each other who they are.

**When:** Dolphins "talk" to each other at night or in the dark. The noise they make bounces off objects around them so that they can tell what not to bump into!

**Why:** Dolphins "talk" to identify each other and to "see" in the dark.

**How:** Each dolphin has its own unique sound.

**Other information:** Dolphins know each other by name.

Name _____ Date _____

# Complete and Incomplete Sentences

**Focus**
- A **complete sentence** has a subject and a predicate.

- In an **incomplete sentence**, or **fragment**, the subject or predicate is missing.

- A **run-on sentence** is two ideas mixed together.

- To *correct* an **incomplete sentence**, add the missing subject or predicate to the sentence.

Example

**Fragment:** Over one billion vehicles

**Correct:** Over one billion vehicles have crossed the bridge.

- To correct a **run-on sentence**, write two sentences.

Example

**Run-On:** The fog covers the bridge it stands over the water.

**Correct:** The fog covers the bridge. It stands over the water.

**Practice** **Write *C* for complete sentence, *F* for fragment, or *R* for run-on.**

**1.** Orange trees plenty of water. _____F_____

**2.** Potatoes grow in cool climates they can't grow in freezing weather. _____R_____

**3.** My family likes to have a garden. _____C_____

**Rewrite each sentence correctly.**

**1.** Orange trees need plenty of water._____

**2.** Potatoes grow in cool climates. They can't grow in freezing weather._____

**3.** My family likes to have a garden._____

**Apply** **Circle the word group that correctly completes each sentence.**

**1.** The first bridges ⟨**were tree trunks.**⟩
**some footbridges.**

**2.** Pontoon bridges **the surface.**
⟨**float on the water.**⟩

**3.** Arches ⟨**are very strong.**⟩
**curved supports.**

**Name** _____     **Date** _____

# /ā/ Sound and Spellings

**Focus**
- The /ā/ sound can be spelled with *ai_* and *_ay*.
- The *ai_* pattern is usually in the front or middle of a word.
- The *_ay* pattern is usually found at the end of a word.

**Practice**   Read the following words aloud.

| aim | paint | okay | display |
|-----|-------|------|---------|
| rain | away | waist | today |

**Write the words with the /ā/ sound spelled like *aid*.**

1. _____aim_____       3. _____rain_____

2. _____paint_____     4. _____waist_____

**Write the words with the /ā/ sound spelled like *way*.**

1. _____okay_____      3. _____away_____

2. _____display_____   4. _____today_____

**Apply**  Choose a word from the box to complete each sentence. Write the word on the line.

| bait | braid | holiday | sway | explain |
|------|-------|---------|------|---------|
| away | wait | spray | daisy | maybe |

1. What is your favorite _____holiday_____?

2. Can you _____braid_____ my hair?

3. The teacher will _____explain_____ the assignment.

4. Linda put _____bait_____ on her fishing hook.

5. Grandpa picked a _____daisy_____ for me.

6. I can't _____wait_____ to go to the circus.

7. Everyone needs to put the toys _____away_____.

8. _____Maybe_____ we should eat lunch now.

9. I saw a tree _____sway_____ in the breeze.

10. Don't forget to _____spray_____ water on the plant.

Name _____ Date _____

# /ā/ Sound and Spellings

**Focus**  •The /ā/ sound can be spelled with *a* and *a_e*.

**Practice** Unscramble the following words. Write the word on the line and write *a* or *a_e* to tell the spelling pattern.

1. a p e r p    paper                a
2. l a p e t    plate                a_e
3. a y z l      lazy                 a
4. r e d a t    trade                a_e
5. s l e a c    scale                a_e
6. c b e l a    cable                a

**Write a sentence using a word with each spelling pattern from above.** Possible answers below.

I feel lazy today.

Sally dropped the plate.

**Apply** Choose a word from the box that makes sense in the sentence. Write the word on the line.

**1.** Breakfast is the most important meal of the day.

This morning, I _____ate_____ oatmeal.

I also had a piece of _____bacon_____.

| table |
| bacon |
| ate |

**2.** We went to the bakery Saturday morning.

Mom let me _____taste_____ a doughnut.

Then, I ate a _____bagel_____.

| bagel |
| pastry |
| taste |

**3.** Reading is my favorite thing to do.

My teacher is reading a _____fable_____.

It is about a sneaky _____snake_____.

| fable |
| snake |
| movie |

**4.** A newspaper has a lot of interesting stories.

My family gets the _____daily_____ paper.

The front _____page_____ stories are interesting.

| story |
| page |
| daily |

Name _____ Date _____

# Selection Vocabulary

**Focus**

**chain** *n.* A row of connected or related circles.

**fossil** *n.* Preserved remains.

**trace** *v.* To follow the path of something.

**outstretched** *adj.* Reaching out.

**print** *n.* A mark made by pressing.

**Practice** **Match each word on the left to its definition on the right.**

**1.** fossil

**2.** trace

**3.** outstretched

**4.** chain

**5.** print

**a.** a row of connected or related circles

**b.** preserved remains

**c.** a mark made by pressing

**d.** to follow the path of something

**e.** reaching out

**Write two sentences using at least one vocabulary word in each sentence.** Possible answers below.

**1.** I traced around my hand to make a picture.

**2.** Lewis found a fossil on the rock

 **Apply** Use the vocabulary words to complete each sentence.

| chain | trace | print | fossil | outstretched |

1. The dog's collar was connected to a _____chain_____.

2. I saw a _____fossil_____ at the museum.

3. _____Trace_____ the letter with your finger.

4. Brandi made a leaf _____print_____.

5. His arm was _outstretched_ to reach the light.

**Write the vocabulary word you think of after reading each word or words.**

1. leaf or shell _____print_____

2. circles _____chain_____

3. follow _____trace_____

4. remains _____fossil_____

5. reaching _outstretched_

Name _____ Date _____

# Compare and Contrast

**Focus**
- To **compare** means to tell how things, events, or characters are alike in some way.

- To **contrast** means to tell how things, events, or characters are **different**.

- **Clue words** help show how things are alike and different.

### Clue Words

| Alike | | Different |
|-------|-----|-----------|
| both | as | different |
| same | too | but |
| like | | |

**Practice**  Circle whether the sentence is comparing or contrasting. Write the clue word on the line.

1. Uncle Joe has a collection of rocks, just like me.

   (compare)     contrast     _____like_____

2. Our collections are very different in size.

   compare     (contrast)     _____different_____

**Apply** Use the chart below to compare an apple and a banana. Write three ways these foods are alike and three ways that they are different. Possible answers below.

## Apple and Banana

| Compare (alike) | Contrast (different) |
|---|---|
| 1. both are food | 1. apple is red, banana is yellow |
| 2. both grow on trees | 2. taste different |
| 3. both are fruit | 3. apple is round, banana is long and skinny |

Use the lists above to help you write a sentence to compare these things and a sentence to contrast them. Underline the clue word used in each sentence. Possible answers below.

*Compare*

An apple and a banana are <u>both</u> fruit.

*Contrast*

An apple and a banana have <u>different</u> tastes.

Name _____ Date _____

# Writing a Comparison

 **Audience: Who** will read your comparison?

_____

**Purpose: What** is your reason for writing your comparison?

_____

**Prewriting** **Use this Venn diagram to organize your compare and contrast paragraphs.**

Possible answers below.

| Different | Alike | Different |
|---|---|---|
| Rocks are nonliving. | Both tell you information. | Ants are living things. |
| You can use rocks to do different things. | They talk about things found in nature. | Ants live in colonies. |
| Rocks can be all different sizes. | Photographs used in books. | Ants can build their home. |

## Revising    Use this checklist to revise.

☐ Did you include a topic sentence that names the two stories?

☐ Did you compare and contrast the two stories?

☐ Does the first paragraph compare the stories?

☐ Does the second paragraph begin with a transition sentence?

☐ Does the second paragraph contrast the stories?

☐ Did you use clue words?

☐ Will the reader understand the information?

## Editing/Proofreading    Use this checklist to correct mistakes.

☐ Is each paragraph indented?

☐ Make sure all of your sentences are complete.

☐ Is every word or special term spelled correctly?

☐ Does every sentence start with a capital letter and end with correct punctuation?

## Publishing    Use this checklist to prepare for publication.

☐ Write or type a neat copy.

☐ Include a drawing of the two things in the comparison.

Name _____ Date _____

# Long vowel a spelled *ai_*, *_ay*, *a*, and *a_e*

**Focus**
- Long vowel a sounds like the letter a.
- Some ways that the long a sound can be spelled are *ai_*, *_ay*, *a*, and *a_e*.

**Practice** **Sort the spelling words under the correct heading.**

long a spelled *ai_*

1. rain
2. chain
3. paid

long a spelled *_ay*

4. stay
5. play
6. May

long a spelled *a*

7. April
8. fable

long a spelled *a_e*

9. base
10. trace

**Word List**

1. stay
2. rain
3. base
4. April
5. May
6. chain
7. trace
8. play
9. paid
10. fable

**Challenge Words**

11. waist
12. railroad
13. pavement
14. flavor
15. Thursday

**Rhyming Strategy** Write the spelling word that rhymes with each set of words below. The new word should have the same spelling pattern for the long a sound.

11. day     ray     <u>stay OR play OR may</u>

12. cable     stable     <u>fable</u>

13. aid     maid     <u>paid</u>

14. chase     case     <u>base</u>

15. main     stain     <u>rain OR chain</u>

**Proofreading Strategy** Circle the misspelled words. Rewrite the words correctly below.

One of my favorite months is the month of (Mai.) In the month of (Ayprul), there is always a lot of (rayn), so you must (plai) indoors. Once May comes, I like to do outdoor activities, like making a daisy (chane). I cannot wait for next May to come!

16. <u>May</u>

17. <u>April</u>

18. <u>rain</u>

19. <u>play</u>

20. <u>chain</u>

Name _____ Date _____

# Using the Card Catalog

**Focus**
- The **card catalog** is a system for finding books in the library.
- Every catalog card has a call number, the name of the book, the author's name, a summary, and a cross-reference.

**Practice** Find and mark these items on the card catalog card shown:
- **Circle the call number.**
- **Draw a line under the author's name.**
- **Draw two lines under the title.**
- **Put a check mark by the summary.**

[E
(599.74422BEN]

Bender, Lionel

Lions and Tigers

New York, Gloucester Press, c. 1988
       [31] p.
Summary: Describes the habits and behaviors of lions and
             tigers, with a discussion of how they survive. ✓
1. lions    2. tigers

**Apply** Use the card or computer catalog to find one book on a subject you are interested in. Write the call number, the author's name, and the book title on the lines below. Then take the paper with you as you look for the book.

Possible answers below.

Call Number: __595.44 ALL__

Author's Name: __Allen, Judy__

Book Title: __Are You a Spider?__

**Answer the following questions.**

**1.** Did you find the book? __yes__

**2.** Did you find the information from the card catalog helpful? Why? __Yes. I was able to find the book quickly.__

**3.** Why do you think the card catalog is important to have in a library? __Because there are so many books in the library, you need an easy way to find what you are looking for.__

Name _____  Date _____

# Kinds of Sentences

**Focus**

- There are different kinds of sentences.
- A **declarative sentence** makes a statement. It always ends with a period (.).

Example
    Mars is a planet.

- An **interrogative sentence** asks a question. It always ends in a question mark (?).

Example
    Will people ever live on Mars?

- An **imperative sentence** gives directions or a command. It always ends in a period (.).

Example
    Begin the countdown now.

- An **exclamatory sentence** shows strong feelings. It always ends in an exclamation mark (!).

Example
    What a perfect launch!

**Practice**  **Read each sentence below. Write the type of sentence on the line.**

**1.** Pick up that rock. _____imperative_____

**2.** Did you find any rocks today? _____interrogative_____

**Name** _____ **Date** _____

# End Marks

 **Focus**
- Every sentence needs to end with a punctuation, or **end mark**.

- A statement or direction should end with a **period** (.).

Example
  It will rain today.

- A question should end with a **question mark** (?).

Example
  Do you have an umbrella?

- A sentence that shows strong feelings should end with an **exclamation point** (!).

Example
  Look out for that puddle!

**Practice** **Put the correct end mark at the end of each sentence.**

**1.** Where does snow come from ?

**2.** Icy droplets of water in clouds turn into snowflakes .

**3.** It's amazing that no two snowflakes are alike !

**4.** Where do the water droplets come from ?

**5.** They come from Earth's lakes, rivers, and oceans .

Grammar • *Skills Practice 1*

**Name** _____ **Date** _____

# /ē/ Sound and Spellings

 **Focus** • The /ē/ sound can be spelled with *ee, ea, e,* and *e_e.*

**Practice** **Underline the /ē/ spellings in the words below. Some words have two spellings for /ē/.**

1. r<u>e</u>p<u>ea</u>t

2. b<u>e</u>tw<u>ee</u>n

3. l<u>e</u>gal

4. s<u>ea</u>w<u>ee</u>d

5. d<u>e</u>l<u>e</u>t<u>e</u>

6. compl<u>e</u>t<u>e</u>

7. r<u>e</u>move

8. extr<u>e</u>m<u>e</u>

9. r<u>e</u>h<u>ea</u>t

10. d<u>e</u>pend

**Apply** Choose the word that completes each sentence. Write the word on the line.

**1.** I can't ___believe___ it! The snow ___keeps___
(behave, believe)        (keeps, peak)

falling and falling. The ___trees___ look
(trees, only)

really pretty. Mom said ___maybe___ we
(these, maybe)

can go sledding.

**2.** Antoine can't ___decide___ what to do. The
(decide, delay)

talent show is only two ___weeks___ away.
(weekly, weeks)

Antoine can juggle ___bean___ bags.
(bean, beet)

He also does a ___pretend___ show with his
(pretend, the)

___zebra___ puppet. Which would
(theme, zebra)

___be___ better?
(me, be)

**Name** _____  **Date** _____

# /ā/ Sound and Spellings

**Focus** • The /ā/ sound can be spelled with *ai_*, *_ay*, *a*, and *a_e*.

**Practice** **Read the word in the box. Then read the sentence. Change the word in the box to make a new rhyming word to complete the sentence.**

1. | **same** | The opposite of *wild* is ___tame___.

2. | **say** | Mixing black and white makes ___gray___.

3. | **fair** | Shoes come in a ___pair___.

4. | **hay** | The waiter carried a big ___tray___.

5. | **whale** | The store is having a ___sale___.

6. | **cage** | Turn the ___page___ and keep reading.

7. | **gain** | Let's ride the ___train___ into the city.

8. | **sway** | We like to ___play___ kickball at recess.

9. | **save** | A ___wave___ washed away our sandcastle.

10. | **stair** | Jamal sat in a ___chair___ at the front of the room.

**Apply**  Read each sentence. Circle the word that correctly completes the sentence.

**1.** James wants to _____ the leaves into a big pile.
   **a.** rake   **b.** rayke   **c.** rak

**2.** If the _____ doesn't stop, we can play inside.
   **a.** raine   **b.** rane   **c.** rain

**3.** We made _____ pots in art class.
   **a.** claiy   **b.** clay   **c.** claye

**4.** The _____ is locked each night at 9:00.
   **a.** gayt   **b.** gate   **c.** gait

**5.** Do you like red or green _____?
   **a.** grapes   **b.** graips   **c.** graypes

**6.** A monkey has a _____, but an ape does not.
   **a.** tayl   **b.** tail   **c.** taile

**7.** Mother's Day is in the month of _____.
   **a.** Mai   **b.** Mae   **c.** May

**8.** A _____ of black horses pulled the wagon.
   **a.** payr   **b.** pair   **c.** pare

**9.** We cannot _____ on the sidewalk.
   **a.** skat   **b.** skait   **c.** skate

**10.** Get a pump to _____ the flat tire.
   **a.** inflate   **b.** inflait   **c.** inflat

Name _____ Date _____

# Selection Vocabulary

**Focus**

**sensing** *v.* Feeling.

**dull** *adj.* Not bright or clear.

**antennae** *n.* Plural of **antenna:** an insect feeler.

**cycle** *n.* A repeated sequence of events.

**fussy** *adj.* Hard to please.

**Practice** **Choose a vocabulary word from above that matches each definition.**

1. <u>fussy</u> hard to please

2. <u>dull</u> not bright or clear

3. <u>sensing</u> feeling

4. <u>cycle</u> a repeated sequence of events

5. <u>antennae</u> insect feelers

**Apply** Circle the word in parentheses that best fits each sentence.

1. Keith is not (**fussy,** dull) about the food he eats.

2. Different animals can (antennae, **sense**) danger.

3. (**Dull,** Sensing) colors can help some insects hide.

4. Count the (cycle, **antennae**) on the grasshopper's head.

5. Explain a grasshopper's life (**cycle,** fussy).

**Draw a picture of a grasshopper. Write three sentences about a grasshopper using at least one vocabulary word in each sentence.** Possible answers below.

1. Grasshoppers use their antennae to touch and smell things.

2. Grasshoppers are not fussy about what they eat.

3. Grasshoppers have dull outer wings.

Name _____ Date _____

# Writing a Summary

 **Think**

**Audience: Who** will read your summary?

_____

**Purpose: What** is your reason for writing your summary?

_____

**Prewriting** **Use the graphic organizer to organize the notes for your summary.** Possible answers below.

| Topic: |
|---|
| dinosaur fossils |

| Subtopic: | Subtopic: | Subtopic: | Subtopic: |
|---|---|---|---|
| scientists learn about dinosaurs from their fossils | plants and animals that are covered by mud and sand harden into rock | scientists study fossils | fossils tell how each type of dinosaur was different |

**Conclusion:**
Every time someone finds a fossil, we learn more about life on Earth long ago.

## Revising  Use this checklist to revise.

☐ Did you tell the main idea and details?

☐ Did you use your own words?

☐ Is there information that is not from the book or article?

☐ Will the reader understand the information?

☐ Did you write a conclusion to your summary?

## Editing/Proofreading  Use this checklist to correct mistakes.

☐ Make sure all of your sentences are complete.

☐ Is every word or special term spelled correctly?

☐ Does every sentence start with a capital letter and end with correct punctuation?

## Publishing  Use this checklist to prepare for publication.

☐ Write or type a neat copy.

☐ Add a photograph or drawing.

Name _____ Date _____

# Long vowel a spelled *ai_, _ay, a, a_e*
# Long vowel e spelled *ee, ea, e, e_e*

**Focus**
- Long vowels sound like their names.
- Long a can be spelled *ai_, _ay, a,* and *a_e.*
- Long e can be spelled *ee, ea, e,* and *e_e.*

**Word List**

1. tail
2. reach
3. queen
4. fear
5. say
6. gave
7. sweet
8. acorn
9. player
10. even

**Challenge Words**

11. underneath
12. always
13. depend
14. wait
15. sneeze

**Practice** **Sort the spelling words under the correct heading.**

long a spelled *ai_*

1. tail

long a spelled *_ay*

2. say

3. player

long a spelled *a*

4. acorn

long a spelled *a_e*

5. gave

long e spelled *ee*

6. queen

7. sweet

long e spelled *ea*

8. reach

9. fear

long e spelled *e*

10. even

**Apply** Consonant-Substitution Strategy Replace the underlined letter to create a spelling word. Then write the new word.

11. <u>s</u>ail + t = tail

12. swee<u>p</u> + t = sweet

13. <u>b</u>each + r = reach

14. sa<u>d</u> + y = say

15. <u>t</u>ear + f = fear

Visualization Strategy Circle the correct spelling for each spelling word. Write the correct spelling on the line.

16. eavun (even) even

17. (queen) qween queen

18. (gave) gav gave

19. playur (player) player

20. (acorn) akorn acorn

**Name** _____ **Date** _____

# Table of Contents/Index

**Focus**
- You can find all kinds of important information in books when you know where to look.

- The **Table of Contents** is located in the front of a book. It is an organized list of the chapters and their page numbers.

- An **Index** is located in the back of a book. It is a detailed list of important words and phrases from the book. The words are in alphabetical order and a page number is included.

**Practice** **Find a partner and decide on a book to use for the following activities.**

**1.** Write the title of the book you chose.

_____

**2.** How many chapters are in this book?

_____

**3.** Choose one topic from this book and write down the page numbers where it can be found in the book.

_____

**Apply** **Use the table of contents and the index in books to help you find the information you are looking for. Do the following:**

• First, find a book on your subject.

• Then look in the table of contents. Find a chapter that may have information you need.

• Write the chapter title and the page number below. If you find more than one chapter with information you need, write the title and page number of each.

• Think of words that name the information you are looking for. Then look through the index of the book. Find words related to your subject. Write the page numbers.

Book Title: _____

Title of chapters and page numbers with information I need:

_____ Page: _____

_____ Page: _____

Words related to the information I'm looking for and the page numbers from the index:

_____ Page: _____

_____ Page: _____

Name _____ Date _____

# Capitalization: Proper Nouns, Titles, and Initials

**Focus**
- There are many places to use capital letters.
- A **proper noun** names a particular person, place, or thing. A proper noun always begins with a capital letter.

Example
> **Alaska** is the biggest state in the **United States**.

- **Titles** in people's names begin with capital letters.

Example
> **Mr.** Tilly told us to form a straight line.
> **Dr.** Jilly gave me a checkup today.

- **Initials** from people's names are capitalized.

Example
> **E.B.** White is the author of *Stuart Little*.

**Practice** Underline three times each proper noun, title, or set of initials that should be capitalized in the sentences below.

1. John adams and John q. adams were both presidents of the united states of america.

2. The president of the united states is called mr. President.

3. Presidents t. roosevelt and franklin d. Roosevelt were cousins.

**Apply** **Write an initial or title in the blank.** Possible answers below.

**1.** Our family doctor is ____Dr. Laurel____.

**2.** The soccer coach at our school is ____Mr./Miss/Mrs.____ Watson.

**3.** The gorilla at the zoo was named ____Mr./Miss/Mrs.____ Big.

**4.** The vet who takes care of our cats is named

____Dr. Tawney____.

**5.** Did you ever see Jeff's dad, ____Mr. Cole____?

**Read the story below. Underline three times the proper nouns, titles, and initials that should be capitalized.**

The architect i̲. m̲. p̲ei was born in c̲hina in

1917. m̲r. p̲ei has designed many large, beautiful

buildings. In 1960, he designed the terminal at

j̲f̲k̲ international airport in n̲ew y̲ork. A landscape

architect designs gardens and outdoor spaces. The

first person to call himself a landscape architect

was f̲. l̲. o̲lmsted.

**Name** _____  **Date** _____

# /ē/ Sound and Spellings

**Focus**
- The /ē/ sound can be spelled with _ie_, _y, and _ey.

- The _ie_ pattern is usually found in the middle of a word.

- The _y and _ey patterns are usually found at the end of a word.

**Practice**  **Read each word. Underline the spelling pattern used in each word.**

**1.** sh<u>ie</u>ld

**4.** man<u>y</u>

**2.** alle<u>y</u>

**5.** valle<u>y</u>

**3.** prett<u>y</u>

**6.** gr<u>ie</u>f

**Choose one of the spelling patterns listed to complete each word. Write the pattern in the word and then write the word on the blank line.**

**1.** lad__y__    _____lady_____

**2.** ch__ie__f    _____chief_____

**3.** donk__ey__    _____donkey_____

**Apply** **Read the sentence. Choose the word that completes the sentence. Write the word on the line.**

1. The ___thief___ stole the diamond ring.

   thief   thefe   theyfe

2. My glass of milk is now ___empty___.

   emptie   empty   emptee

3. We watched the ___monkey___ eat a banana.

   monkie   monkee   monkey

4. There are flowers growing in the ___field___.

   feeld   field   feyld

5. How much ___money___ is in the piggy bank?

   money   monie   mony

6. A four-leaf clover is a ___lucky___ thing to find.

   lucky   luckie   luckey

7. The ___baby___ played with her rattle.

   babee   baby   babie

8. Bees keep ___honey___ in their hive.

   honie   hony   honey

9. Can I have a ___piece___ of fruit?

   piece   peyce   pyce

10. Will you read a ___story___ to me?

    storie   storey   story

Phonics • *Skills Practice 1*

Name _____   Date _____

# /ē/ Sound and Spellings

**Focus**
- The /ē/ sound can be spelled with *ee*, *ea*, *e*, and *e_e*.

**Practice** Underline the spelling pattern used in each word. Write the pattern and a new word with the same spelling pattern. The words do not have to rhyme.

1. scr<u>ee</u>n ___ee___ ___meet___
2. d<u>e</u>vice ___e___ ___zebra___
3. h<u>ea</u>t ___ea___ ___seal___
4. f<u>ee</u>l ___ee___ ___feed___
5. concr<u>e</u>t<u>e</u> ___e_e___ ___complete___
6. sn<u>ee</u>ze ___ee___ ___breeze___
7. r<u>e</u>cent ___e___ ___decent___
8. t<u>ea</u>ch ___ea___ ___reach___
9. <u>e</u>v<u>e</u> ___e_e___ ___Steve___
10. sp<u>ea</u>k ___ea___ ___weak___

 **Apply** Choose a word from the box to complete each sentence. Write the word on the line.

| | | | |
|---|---|---|---|
| fifteen | seasons | pretending | here |
| tepee | evening | disappear | weeds |

**1.** Winter, Spring, Summer, and Autumn are the four

_____seasons_____.

**2.** We are _____pretending_____ to be princesses.

**3.** Did you put the flashlight over _____here_____?

**4.** The number after fourteen is _____fifteen_____.

**5.** Hannah and Jack pulled the _____weeds_____ from the garden.

**6.** My friends and I made a _____tepee_____ in my yard.

**7.** Is the play this _____evening_____?

**8.** The magician made the coin _____disappear_____.

Name _____ Date _____

# Selection Vocabulary

**Focus**

**rent** *n.* A regular payment for the right to use equipment or property that belongs to someone else.

**deserted** *v.* Past tense of **desert**: to leave something behind.

**vacant** *adj.* Empty.

**tenants** *n.* Plural of **tenant**: one who lives in or on another person's property.

**examined** *v.* Past tense of **examine**: to look at closely and carefully.

**Practice** **Circle the correct word that completes each sentence.**

1. When no one lived in the birdhouse, it was _____.
   **a.** examined   (**b.** vacant)   **c.** rent

2. Mr. Chickadee _____ the house closely.
   (**a.** examined)   **b.** deserted   **c.** vacant

3. The sign said "Birdhouse for _____".
   **a.** tenants   **b.** deserted   (**c.** rent)

4. Mrs. Chickadee stayed outside and _____ her eggs.
   (**a.** deserted)   **b.** rent   **c.** tenants

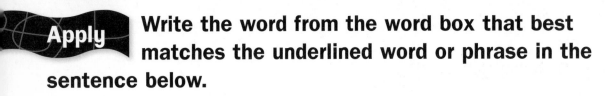

**Apply** Write the word from the word box that best matches the underlined word or phrase in the sentence below.

| rent | vacant | examined | desert | tenant |
|------|--------|----------|--------|--------|

**1.** Each month Bob pays <u>a regular payment for the right to use personal property</u> to the owner of his house.

　　　　rent

**2.** Patty <u>looked at closely and carefully</u> the diamond ring.

　　examined

**3.** We looked around the <u>empty</u> house.

　　vacant

**4.** The cat was forced to <u>leave behind</u> her kittens.

　　desert

**5.** A chipmunk does not make a good <u>someone who lives in or on another person's property</u>.

　　tenant

Name _____ Date _____

# Author's Point of View

**Focus**
- When a story is told by a character in the story, readers see the story through the eyes of that character. The author uses words like *I*, *me*, *mine*, *us*, *our*, and *we*. This is called **first-person point of view.**

- When the story is told by someone who is not part of the story, then the author uses words like *he*, *she*, *it*, *her*, *they*, and *their*. This is called **third-person point of view.**

**Practice**
Circle the word that gives a clue about the author's point of view. Then write first-person point of view or third-person point of view.

**1.** Marsha and (her) mother almost missed the plane. (They) had a hard time getting a taxi to the airport. Luckily, (their) plane was late taking off.

**Point of view:** third-person point of view

**2.** Jamie and (I) shared our snacks. Dad gave (us) apples, sandwiches, and peanuts. (We) ate the snacks at the picnic table.

**Point of view:** first-person point of view

**Apply** **Look at the story "Birdhouse For Rent".**
**What is the point of view?**

first-person point of view

**How do you know?**

The author uses the words I and my.

**Who is telling the story?**

the birdhouse

**Find an example in which the storyteller shares thoughts and feelings. Write it below.** Possible answer below.

"Oh what messy tenants!"

**Write a short sentence about something that happened in school from a first-person point of view. Then rewrite the sentence from a third-person point of view.**
Possible answer below.

1. Yesterday my class took a field trip to the apple orchard.

2. Mrs. Jones and her class took a field trip to the apple orchard.

Name _____ Date _____

# Writing a Comparison

**Think** Audience: **Who** will read your comparison?

_____

Purpose: **What** is your reason for writing your
comparison?

_____

**Prewriting** Compare two animals of your choice. Use the
Venn diagram to organize your ideas.

Possible answers below.

**Different**     **Alike**     **Different**

Snowy Owl

stays
white all
year to
match the
snow

both owls match
their surroundings

Screech
Owl

matches
the bark of
a tree

## Revising  Use this checklist to revise.

☐ Did you clearly compare and contrast two animals?

☐ Does your writing contain facts about your topic?

☐ Did you use clue words to compare and contrast?

☐ Does the first paragraph compare the animals?

☐ Does the second paragraph begin with a transition sentence?

☐ Does the second paragraph contrast the animals?

☐ Will the reader understand the information?

## Editing/Proofreading  Use this checklist to correct mistakes.

☐ Is each paragraph indented?

☐ Make sure all of your sentences are complete.

☐ Is every word or special term spelled correctly?

☐ Does every sentence start with a capital letter and end with correct punctuation?

## Publishing  Use this checklist to prepare for publication.

☐ Write or type a neat copy.

☐ Include your diagram and pictures of the two animals.

Name _____  Date _____

# The /s/ sound spelled ce and ci_
# The /j/ sound spelled ge and gi_

**Focus**
- Two ways that the /s/ sound can be spelled are ce and ci_.
- Two ways that the /j/ sound can be spelled are ge and gi_.

**Practice**  **Sort the spelling words under the correct heading.**

**/s/ spelled ce**

1. peace
2. ice
3. face

**/j/ spelled ge**

6. age
7. gem
8. large

**/s/ spelled ci_**

4. pencil
5. circus

**/j/ spelled gi_**

9. magic
10. digit

**Word List**
1. age
2. peace
3. pencil
4. magic
5. ice
6. digit
7. face
8. gem
9. circus
10. large

**Challenge Words**
11. piece
12. gentle
13. tragic
14. century
15. excite

**Apply** **Meaning Strategy** Write the spelling word next to its meaning clue.

1. Something that you write with __pencil__

2. A feeling of calm and quiet __peace__

3. Frozen water __ice__

4. How old someone is __age__

**Visualization Strategy** Circle the correct spelling for each spelling word. Write the correct spelling on the line.

1. majic   (magic)   majic _____

2. serkus   (circus)   circus _____

3. (face)   fase   face _____

4. (digit)   dijit   digit _____

5. (large)   larj   large _____

6. jem   (gem)   gem _____

Name _____ Date _____

# Adjectives

**Focus**

- An **adjective** is a word that describes a noun. An adjective tells *how much*, *how many*, or *what kind*.

Example

There are **five** classes of **living** things.

- Articles are special kinds of adjectives. There are three articles: *a*, *an*, and *the*.

Example

**An** insect or **a** bird might be included in **the** animal class.

**Practice**  **Read the poem below. Circle the adjectives and articles.**

For (a) (big) (green) plant

Or (a) (tiny) (little) ant

Resting in (the) woods is nice.

Each (living) thing must

Share (cool) shade and just

Take (a) break in paradise.

**Apply** Circle the adjectives and underline the articles in the sentences below.

**1.** A duck likes to spend time in the water.

**2.** (Clumsy) swans find it hard to walk on the ground.

**3.** Raptors have (pointed) beaks to tear things.

**4.** A penguin uses its wings to swim in the ocean.

**5.** (Large) ostriches can be as big as eight feet tall.

**Read the paragraph below. Underline the articles and circle the adjectives.**

Many creatures live in the forest. (Blue)

peacocks and (brown) owls live in the forests. (Red)

deer and (gray) squirrels live there, too. (Green) frogs

live in the forests that are near water. Sometimes,

a (white) rabbit can be found hopping through the

forest. How many bears have you seen in the

forest? I saw (two) bears last year.

Name _____ Date _____

# /s/ Sound and Spellings

**Focus** • The /s/ sound can be spelled *ce*, *ci_*, and *cy*.

**Practice** **Read each word aloud. Underline the spelling pattern that makes the /s/ sound.**

**1.** i<u>ce</u>

**2.** poli<u>cy</u>

**3.** pen<u>ci</u>l

**4.** <u>ce</u>nter

**5.** la<u>cy</u>

**6.** <u>ci</u>ty

**7.** tra<u>ce</u>

**8.** <u>ci</u>vil

**Use the words in the box to complete each sentence.**

| rice | circle | fancy | juicy | circus |
|------|--------|-------|-------|--------|

**1.** Draw a square, triangle, and _____circle_____.

**2.** Patsy has a _____fancy_____ dress.

**3.** The watermelon was very _____juicy_____.

**4.** May I please have more _____rice_____?

**5.** We went to the _____circus_____.

 **Apply** Choose a word from the box that makes sense in the sentence. Write the word on the line.

**1.** We went out to eat dinner.

The pizza was in the shape of a

large ___circle___.

I ate three ___slices___.

| circle |
| fancy |
| slices |

**2.** My sister loves going to school.

___Nancy___ is in the ninth grade.

Her favorite subject is ___science___.

| space |
| science |
| Nancy |

**3.** Rebecca enjoys spending time with her family.

She lives in the same ___city___
as her brother.

Rebecca's ___niece___ likes to play with her.

| niece |
| city |
| race |

**4.** Ned goes to see a movie every Saturday.

A fancy name for a movie is ___cinema___.

Today's movie is about two funny ___mice___.

| circus |
| mice |
| cinema |

Name _____   Date _____

# /j/ Sound and Spellings

**Focus** • The /j/ sound can be spelled *ge* and *gi_*.

**Practice** Read each word aloud.  Underline the spelling pattern that makes the /j/ sound.

1. ra<u>ge</u>          5. crin<u>ge</u>

2. lo<u>gi</u>c          6. <u>gi</u>raffe

3. <u>gi</u>ant          7. oran<u>ge</u>

4. <u>ge</u>ntle          8. fra<u>gi</u>le

Draw a line connecting one word on the left with a rhyming word on the right.

1. budge          **a.** magic

2. cage          **b.** fudge

3. twinge          **c.** frigid

4. tragic          **d.** page

5. rigid          **e.** hinge

**Apply** Look at the pairs of words below. Choose the word that best completes the sentence and write the word on the line.

**1.** Angela left a _____message_____ for you.
(message, messagi)

**2.** The car's _____engine_____ is making funny sounds.
(engene, engine)

**3.** 153 is a three-_____digit_____ number.
(digit, diget)

**4.** Use your _____imagination_____ to write a story.
(imagenation, imagination)

**5.** My aunt lives in a tiny _____cottage_____.
(cottage, cottagi)

**6.** Park the car in our _____garage_____.
(garagi, garage)

**7.** The glass vase is very _____fragile_____.
(fragele, fragile)

**8.** Did you hear that _____strange_____ sound?
(strange, stangi)

**9.** I would like a _____large_____ drink, please.
(lagi, large)

**10.** We will pay for our things at the cash _____register_____.
(register, regester)

Phonics • *Skills Practice 1*

Name _____  Date _____

# Selection Vocabulary

**Focus**

**trunks** *n.* Plural of **trunk**: the main part of a tree where the branches grow out.

**sprouts** *v.* Begins to grow.

**limbs** *n.* Plural of **limb**: a branch of a tree.

**minerals** *n.* Plural of **mineral**: something found underground and used as food for plants growing in soil.

**stems** *n.* Plural of **stem**: the main part of a plant.

**Practice**   **Circle *Yes* or *No* if the boldfaced definition of the underlined word in each sentence makes sense.**

1. Initials were carved in the tree's <u>trunk</u>.
   **main part of a tree where the branches grow out** ....(Yes)  No

2. A plant <u>sprouts</u> from a tiny seed.
   **begins to grow** ...................................................(Yes)  No

3. Cut the <u>stems</u> of the flowers.
   **a branch of a tree**............................................. Yes  (No)

4. Roots of a tree get <u>minerals</u> from the soil.
   **begins to grow** ................................................. Yes  (No)

5. Don't hang from that tree <u>limb</u>!
   **a branch of a tree**.............................................(Yes)  No

 **Write the vocabulary word from the word box to complete each sentence.**

| trunk | limbs | stem | sprout | minerals |
|-------|-------|------|--------|----------|

1. Plants get the _____minerals_____ they need from the soil.

2. A hard, woody stem of a tree is called its

   _____trunk_____.

3. Trees _____sprout_____ from the ground as they begin to grow.

4. Along with the trunk, _____limbs_____ are part of a tree's stem.

5. The _____stem_____ is the main part of any plant.

**Answer the following questions.**

What is the name of the hard layer of wood that covers a tree

*trunk*? _____bark_____

What are the two parts of a tree's *stem*?

_____trunk and limbs_____

Name _____ Date _____

# Classify and Categorize

**Focus**
- **Classifying** and **categorizing** means putting things into groups.

- Readers sort information into different groups or **categories**.

- **Classifying** can help readers keep track of information in the story. To classify information:
  - name the categories for things, characters, or events
  - list the things, characters, or events that fit under each category
  - sometimes things, characters, or events can fit into more than one category

**Practice** Make a list for each category below.
Possible answers below.

**Things I like to do**
1. play soccer
2. video games
3. read
4. ride my bike

**Things I don't like to do**
1. homework
2. chores
3. babysit
4. shop

*Skills Practice 1* • Comprehension

 **Apply** **Read the following paragraph.**

Tree leaves can come in many shapes and sizes. However, there are only two different groups of trees. One group is evergreen and the other group is broadleaf. Most evergreen trees have needles that are thin and scale-like. Some examples of evergreen trees are spruce, cypress, pine, and hemlock. Broadleaf trees have flatter, wider leaves. Beech, maple, oak, and hickory are types of broadleaf trees.

**Use the chart below to classify and categorize the information in the paragraph.**

### Types of Trees

| Category: evergreen | Category: broadleaf |
|---|---|
| 1. spruce | 1. beech |
| 2. pine | 2. maple |
| 3. cypress | 3. oak |
| 4. hemlock | 4. hickory |

Comprehension • *Skills Practice 1*

Name _____ Date _____

# Writing an Informative Report

**Think** **Audience: Who** will read your informative report?

_____

**Purpose: What** is your reason for writing an informative report?

_____

**Prewriting** Plan your report by choosing your topic and asking three questions about your topic. Then write the facts in the web below.

**Question 1:**
Where are the rainforests located?

**Question 2:**
What kinds of plants grow in rainforests?

**Question 3:**
Is it always raining?

**Topic:**
Rainforests

## Revising — Use this checklist to revise.

☐ Did you answer all of your questions?

☐ Do you have one paragraph for each question?

☐ Did you use facts and special words correctly?

☐ Do your ideas and information flow smoothly from one sentence to another?

☐ Is your report written in an interesting, lively way?

## Editing/Proofreading — Use this checklist to correct mistakes.

☐ Is every paragraph indented?

☐ Is every word or special term spelled correctly?

☐ Did you capitalize people's names and place names?

☐ Does every sentence start with a capital letter?

☐ Does every sentence end with correct punctuation?

## Publishing — Use this checklist to prepare for publication.

☐ Write or type a neat copy of your report.

☐ Include a drawing, photograph, or other visual aid to go with your report.

☐ Read your report aloud to the whole class or small groups of classmates.

Name _____ Date _____

# Long e spelled _ie_, _y, ee, ea, e, and e_e
# /s/ spelled ce and ci_
# /j/ spelled ge and gi_

**Focus**
- Long vowels sound like their name.
- The long e sound can be spelled _ie_, _y, ee, ea, e, and e_e.
- The /s/ sound can be spelled ce and ci_.
- The /j/ sound can be spelled ge and gi_.

**Word List**
1. very
2. germ
3. cell
4. civil
5. chief
6. funny
7. thief
8. rigid
9. baby
10. brief

**Challenge Words**
11. grieve
12. cancel

**Practice** Sort the spelling words under the correct heading.

Long e spelled _ie_
1. chief
2. brief
3. thief

Long e spelled _y
4. very
5. funny
6. baby

/j/ spelled ge
7. germ

/j/ spelled gi_
8. rigid

/s/ spelled ce
9. cell

/s/ spelled ci_
10. civil

 **Meaning Strategy**

| very | chief | civil | funny | baby |
|------|-------|-------|-------|------|

**Fill in the blank with a spelling word from the box.**

**1.** People should be _____civil_____ to one another.

**2.** The police _____chief_____ helped train the new recruits.

**3.** The new puppy looked _____funny_____ trying to walk on its hind legs.

**4.** It was _____very_____ hot outside today.

**5.** The _____baby_____ is ready for his bottle.

**Visualization Strategy** Circle the correct spelling for each word. Write the correctly spelled word on the line.

**1.** jurm (germ)    germ _____

**2.** (brief) breef    brief _____

**3.** (thief) theef    thief _____

**4.** celle (cell)    cell _____

**5.** (rigid) rijud    rigid _____

**Name** _____  **Date** _____

# Singular and Plural Nouns

**Focus**

- Nouns can be **singular** or **plural**.
- A **singular noun** names one.

Example
>   star   animal   plant   idea

- **Plural nouns** name more than one.

Example
>   star**s**   animal**s**   plant**s**   idea**s**

- Most nouns add **–s** to form the plural form.

Example
>   car**s**   bike**s**   train**s**

- Some nouns add **–es** to words ending in s, x, z, ss, ch, or sh.

Example
>   brush   brush**es**
>   box   box**es**

- Other nouns ending in y change the y to i and add –es.

Example
>   buddy   budd**ies**

- There are some special nouns. These nouns change when they are made plural.

Example
>   person   people

**Practice** Circle the plural nouns and underline the singular nouns in the sentences below.

1. There is an imaginary line around the middle of our planet.

2. This line is called the equator.

3. The equator divides the earth into two hemispheres.

4. Some parts of the world are always hot.

5. At the equator, climates are hot and rainy.

**Apply** Write the plural form of each noun below.

1. ax     axes

2. rocket     rockets

3. hat     hats

4. man     men

5. sky     skies

6. wish     wishes

    Grammar • *Skills Practice 1*

Name _____ Date _____

# /ī/ Sound and Spellings

**Focus** • The /ī/ sound can be spelled _igh, i, and i_e.

**Practice** Unscramble the following words. Write the word on the first line and the spelling pattern that makes the /ī/ sound on the second line.

**1.** i  d  y  t        tidy                    i

**2.** p  i  e  p        pipe                   i_e

**3.** k  n  d  i        kind                    i

**4.** m  t  e  i        time                   i_e

**5.** g  i  h  h        high                  _igh

**Write a sentence with each word from above.**
Possible answers below.

**1.** I always keep my room tidy.

**2.** The plumber unclogged the pipe.

**3.** The kind girl rescued the lost puppy.

**4.** What time is it?

**5.** The bird was high in the sky.

**Apply**   **Choose a word from the word box to complete each sentence.**

| behind | bite | wide | idea | bright | pile |
|--------|------|------|------|--------|------|

**1.** May I have a _____bite_____ of your dessert?

**2.** Owen had an _____idea_____ of a game to play.

**3.** The sun is _____bright_____ today.

**4.** We all jumped in the _____pile_____ of leaves.

**5.** The opposite of narrow is _____wide_____.

**6.** What is _____behind_____ the curtain?

**Draw a line matching a word on the left to the rhyming word on the right.**

**1.** spiny                **a.** kite

**2.** find                **b.** tight

**3.** white              **c.** tiny

**4.** right               **d.** mind

Name _____ Date _____

# /ī/ Sound and Spellings

**Focus**  • The /ī/ sound can be spelled _y and _ie.

**Practice**  Underline the spelling pattern for the /ī/ sound in each of the following words.

1. sk<u>y</u>          5. tri<u>e</u>d

2. m<u>y</u>          6. sp<u>ie</u>s

3. l<u>ie</u>          7. st<u>y</u>le

4. wh<u>y</u>          8. butterfl<u>y</u>

**Change the first letter to make a new rhyming word. Write the word on the line.** Possible answers below.

1. cry    <u>fry</u>

2. tie    <u>pie</u>

3. why    <u>by</u>

4. fried    <u>tried</u>

 **Apply** Choose a word from the word box to complete each sentence.

| sky | tried | shy | tie | rhyme | fried |
|-----|-------|-----|-----|-------|-------|

**1.** Ethan _____tried_____ to ride his bike.

**2.** My dad put on his _____tie_____.

**3.** Do the words 'night' and 'might' _____rhyme_____?

**4.** The new student seemed to be _____shy_____.

**5.** Can you see the stars in the _____sky_____?

**6.** Angie made _____fried_____ chicken for lunch.

**Add one of the following letters to the words below. Use each letter one time.**

| c | f | l | b | s | p |
|---|---|---|---|---|---|

**1.** _s_py

**2.** _b_y

**3.** _p_ie

**4.** _f_lies

**5.** _l_ie

**6.** _c_ry

Name _____ Date _____

# Selection Vocabulary

**Focus**

**public** *adj.* For all the people.

**automatically** *v.* Working by itself.

**recognize** *v.* To know and remember from before.

**perched** *v.* Past tense of **perch**: to stand, sit, or rest on a raised place.

**practice** *v.* To do something over and over to gain skill.

**Practice** Write the vocabulary word that matches each definition below.

1. _____perched_____ to stand, sit, or rest on a raised place

2. _____practice_____ to do something over and over to gain skill

3. ___automatically___ working by itself

4. _____public_____ for all the people

5. _____recognize_____ to know and remember from before

**Apply** Circle the correct word that completes the sentence.

**1.** A bird was _____ on top of the tree.
  **a.** practice  **b.** perched *(circled)*

**2.** Did you _____ Mr. Williams?
  **a.** recognize *(circled)*  **b.** public

**3.** The traffic light _____ changes colors.
  **a.** recognize  **b.** automatically *(circled)*

**4.** Is the park open to the _____?
  **a.** public *(circled)*  **b.** perched

**5.** Henry will _____ throwing a ball.
  **a.** practice *(circled)*  **b.** recognize

Write the vocabulary word you think of after reading each word.

| public | recognize | practice | automatically | perched |
|---|---|---|---|---|

**1.** rested ___perched___  **4.** itself ___automatically___

**2.** skill ___practice___  **5.** remember ___recognize___

**3.** people ___public___

Name _____  Date _____

# Timed Writing

**Think** **Audience: Who** will read your paragraph?

_____

**Purpose: What** do you want your paragraph to do?

_____

## Timed Writing Strategies

**1.** Read the entire prompt.

**2.** Circle the directions for writing the paper.

**3.** Underline each thing you are asked to write about.

**4.** Read through each reminder.

**5.** Take a few minutes to make notes about your subject.

## Revising  Use this checklist to revise.

☐ Does each sentence help the reader understand your writing?

☐ Did you use specific details?

☐ Are your details organized and in order?

☐ Did you respond to each reminder in the writing prompt?

## Editing/Proofreading  Use this checklist to correct mistakes.

☐ Is your paragraph indented?

☐ Did you use complete sentences?

☐ Is every word or special term spelled correctly?

☐ Does every sentence start with a capital letter?

☐ Does every sentence end with correct punctuation?

**Name** _____ **Date** _____

# Long i spelled _igh, _y, _ie, i, and i_e

**Focus**
- Long vowels sound like their names.
- The long i sound can be spelled _igh, _y, _ie, i, and i_e.

**Practice** **Sort the spelling words under the correct heading.**

long i spelled _igh

1. night
2. right

long i spelled _y

3. fly
4. shy
5. try

long i spelled _ie

6. pie
7. lie

long i spelled i

8. child

long i spelled i_e

9. pile
10. mice

**Word List**
1. pie
2. night
3. fly
4. pile
5. child
6. right
7. shy
8. lie
9. mice
10. try

**Challenge Words**
11. recognize
12. skyscraper
13. style
14. knight
15. mighty

**Apply** Rhyming Strategy Write the spelling word or words that rhyme with each set of words below. The new word will have the same spelling pattern for the long i sound. The first one is done for you.

1. tie     die     pie     lie
2. cry     dry     fly     shy     try
3. dice    twice   mice
4. flight   might   night    right
5. file     mile    pile

Visualization Strategy Circle the correct spelling for each word. Write the correct spelling on the line.

1. nyte    (night)    night
2. (child)   chield    child
3. mighce   (mice)    mice
4. (pie)    py    pie
5. (try)    trie    try

**Name** _____  **Date** _____

# Comparative Adjectives

**Focus**
- An **adjective** describes a noun or pronoun. You can use **comparative adjectives** to compare nouns or pronouns.

- Most adjectives that compare two nouns or pronouns end in **–er**.

- Most adjectives that compare more than two nouns or pronouns end in **–est**.

- Some adjectives use **more** and **most**. Use **more** to compare two things. Use **most** to compare more than two things.

**Practice**  Circle the comparative adjective in each sentence below. Underline the nouns being compared.

**1.** Henry is (taller) than John.

**2.** The parrot is (more) colorful than the robin.

**Apply**  Circle the correct word to complete each sentence.

**1.** You are the _____ girl I know!

luckier  (luckiest)

**2.** Peacocks have the _____ beautiful feathers.

more  (most)

# Articles

**Focus**

• An **adjective** describes a noun or pronoun. **Articles** are special kinds of adjectives.

• The three articles are: *a*, *an*, and *the*.

**Practice** Circle the article in each sentence. Underline the noun it describes.

**1.** (The) play is tomorrow.

**2.** She found (a) dress in her mom's closet.

**3.** She added (an) apron to (the) dress.

**Apply** Write the correct article on the blank line to complete each sentence.

| a | an | the |
|---|----|----|

**1.** Did you find ____a____ coat to wear?

**2.** ____An____ octopus has eight legs.

**3.** Mrs. Jones is ____the____ principal.

Name _____ Date _____

# /ō/ Sound and Spellings

**Focus** • The /ō/ sound can be spelled _ow, and oa_.

**Practice** Use the 'equations' to add (+) and remove (-) letters to create different *ow* and *oa* words.

**1.** glow – g + f = ___flow___ – f + b = ___blow___

**2.** grow – g + c = ___crow___ – c + th = ___throw___

**3.** coat – c + b = ___boat___ – b + m = ___moat___

**4.** road – r + t = ___toad___ – t + l = ___load___

**Write a sentence using one word from each equation above. Circle the spelling pattern in the word you chose for each sentence.** Possible answers below.

**1.** The light had a strange gl(ow).

**2.** Will you thr(ow) the ball to me?

**3.** Let's go for a ride in the b(oa)t.

**4.** Drive down the dirt r(oa)d.

**Apply**   **Read the word in the box. Then read the sentence. Change the word in the box to make a new rhyming word to complete the sentence.**

1. | tow |   Did you _____ mow _____ the lawn today?

2. | hollow |   Did you _____ follow _____ my directions?

3. | coal |   Did you see me score a soccer _____ goal _____?

4. | willow |   Did you use my _____ pillow _____ last night?

5. | roast |   Did you want _____ toast _____ with your eggs?

6. | moan |   Did the bank _____ loan _____ you some money?

7. | fellow |   Did you color the picture of a sun _____ yellow _____?

8. | row |   Did you tie the ribbon into a _____ bow _____?

9. | grow |   Did you see the black _____ crow _____ fly away?

10. | throat |   Did you watch the boat _____ float _____ on the water?

Name _____ Date _____

# /ō/ Sound and Spellings

**Focus** • The /ō/ sound can be spelled o, and o_e.

**Practice** **Use the letters in parentheses ( ) to add to the given spelling pattern to make a word. The letters in parentheses ( ) do not have to go in the order that they are written. Write the new word on the line.**

**1.** (s, m, t)      __ **o** __ __      ___most___

**2.** (v, t)      __ **o** __ e      ___vote___

**3.** (s, t, p)      __ **o** __ __      ___post___

**4.** (c, k, h, e)      __ __ **o** __ e      ___choke___

**Change the word in the box to make a new rhyming word that will complete the sentence.**

**1.** | mow | The car broke down so we had to call a
___tow___ truck.

**2.** | oats | We hang our ___coats___ on the hooks on the wall.

**3.** | note | Ally ___wrote___ a letter to her Uncle Joe.

 **Apply** **Choose a word from the box to complete each sentence.**

| motion | solo | close | whole | over |
|--------|------|-------|-------|------|
| oval | soda | slope | frozen | those |

1. Mariah is going to sing a _____ solo _____ at the concert.

2. Would you like a glass of milk instead of _____ soda _____ to drink?

3. We have to clean up this _____ whole _____ mess quickly!

4. John can draw a circle, square, triangle, and _____ oval _____.

5. Peter forgot to _____ close _____ the door.

6. We can ice skate on the _____ frozen _____ lake.

7. Do _____ those _____ shoes belong to you?

8. Let's ski down the bunny _____ slope _____.

9. Is the movie _____ over _____ already?

10. The _____ motion _____ of the boat made me seasick.

Name _____ Date _____

# Selection Vocabulary

**Focus**

**employees** *n.* Plural of **employee**: a person who works for a person or business for pay.

**borrow** *v.* To receive something with the understanding that it must be given back.

**deposits** *n.* Plural of **deposit**: money added to a bank account.

**vault** *n.* A room or compartment that is used to store money or other things of value.

**withdrawals** *n.* Plural of **withdrawal**: money taken out of a bank account.

**Practice** **Write the vocabulary word that will complete each sentence.**

1. There are many ___employees___ working at the bank.

2. People ___borrow___ money from the bank to buy big items.

3. ___Deposits___ are made when you add money to your account.

4. When you take money out of your account, it is a ___withdrawal___.

5. The ___vault___ is a safe place to store important things.

**Apply** Use your knowledge of the vocabulary words from this lesson to complete the following activities.

Possible answers below.

**1.** Write two examples of jobs done by bank *employees*.

waiting on customers, putting
money in the ATM machine

**2.** What is something you may buy that you would need to *borrow* money from the bank to purchase?

a house

**3.** These are your *deposits*: $10.00, $10.00, and $5.00. How much money do you have in your bank account?

$25.00

**4.** Now, if you *withdraw* $5.00, how much money is left in your bank account?

$20.00

**5.** Write an item that you might keep in a bank vault.

diamond jewelry

Name _____ Date _____

# Timed Writing

**Think**

**Audience: Who** will read your paragraph?

_____

**Purpose: What** do you want your paragraph to do?

_____

## Timed Writing Strategies

**1.** Read the entire prompt.

**2.** Circle the directions for writing the paper.

**3.** Underline each thing you are asked to write about.

**4.** Read through each reminder.

**5.** Take a few minutes to make notes about your subject.

## Revising    Use this checklist to revise.

☐ Does each sentence help the reader understand your writing?

☐ Did you use specific details?

☐ Are your details organized and in order?

☐ Did you respond to each reminder in the writing prompt?

## Editing/Proofreading    Use this checklist to correct mistakes.

☐ Is your paragraph indented?

☐ Did you use complete sentences?

☐ Is every word or special term spelled correctly?

☐ Does every sentence start with a capital letter?

☐ Does every sentence end with correct punctuation?

Name _____  Date _____

# Long o spelled _ow, oa_, o, and o_e

**Focus**
- Long vowels sound like their names.
- The long o sound can be spelled _ow, oa_, o, and o_e.

**Practice**  **Sort the spelling words under the correct heading.**

long o spelled _ow          long o spelled o

1. grow                      9. hello

2. know                      long o spelled o_e

3. blow                      10. store

4. show


long o spelled oa_

5. loan

6. boat

7. toad

8. coat

**Word List**
1. store
2. loan
3. grow
4. boat
5. know
6. toad
7. blow
8. coat
9. hello
10. show

**Challenge Words**
11. borrow
12. coast
13. below
14. robot
15. owe

**Apply** Consonant-Substitution Strategy Replace the underlined letter or letters to create a spelling word. The new word will have the same spelling for the long o sound.

**1.** s<u>h</u>ore + st = store

**2.** <u>r</u>oad + t = toad

**3.** <u>gr</u>oan + l = loan

**4.** coa<u>l</u> + t = coat

**5.** <u>g</u>oat + b = boat

| grow | boat | know | blow | show |
|------|------|------|------|------|

**Meaning Strategy** Write the correct spelling word on the line.

**1.** Do you _____know_____ the answer to number 5?

**2.** I had to _____blow_____ up ten balloons for the party.

**3.** The _____boat_____ ride made me feel a little sick.

**4.** My favorite television _____show_____ is on tonight.

**5.** Eating fruits and vegetables will help you _____grow_____ strong and healthy.

Name _____ Date _____

# Capitalization: Days, Months, Cities, and States

**Focus**
- Calendars will help you remember to capitalize the **days** of the week and **months** of the year.
- You must also capitalize names of **cities** and **states**.

 **Practice** Write the name of the day or the month in each sentence below.

**1.** The day before Wednesday is ___Tuesday___.

**2.** New Year's Day is the first of ___January___.

**3.** The last day of the year is in ___December___.

**4.** The day before Friday is ___Thursday___.

**5.** Valentine's Day is in ___February___.

**6.** The day after Friday is ___Saturday___.

**Apply** **Read the poem. Underline three times each letter that should be capitalized.**

Thirty days has september,

april, june, and november;

All the rest have thirty-one.

february has twenty-eight alone;

Save in leap year, at which time,

february's days are twenty-nine.

**Read the paragraph. Underline three times each letter that should be capitalized.**

My class was studying unusual names of cities in the United States. I began my report on february 28, 2006. I read about boulder, colorado. I wonder if the rocks in that city are bigger than the rocks in little rock, arkansas. Do buffaloes really live in buffalo, new york? Does everyone sew in needles, california? I finished my report on march 6, 2006.

Name _____    Date _____

# /ī/ Sound and Spellings

**Focus** • The /ī/ sound can be spelled _igh, _y, and _ie.

**Practice** **Write the correct spelling of each misspelled word.**

**1.** nyte _____ night _____

**2.** trighed _____ tried _____

**3.** drie _____ dry _____

**4.** ty _____ tie _____

**5.** liet _____ light _____

**6.** shigh _____ shy _____

**Apply** **Choose a word from above to complete the sentence.**

**1.** Lenny _____ tried _____ his best.

**2.** Her dog is _____ shy _____.

**3.** I went shopping last _____ night _____.

**Practice** Choose a letter below to fill in the beginning blank of the words below. Write the word on the line.

| i | t | s | l |
|---|---|---|---|

1. ___t___ire          ___tire___

2. ___i___dol          ___idol___

3. ___l___iar          ___liar___

4. ___s___ize          ___size___

**Apply** Choose a word from the box that makes sense in the sentence. Write the word on the line.

1. What can you do on a windy day?

   Try flying a ___kite___.

   It will look like a ___tiny___ dot in the sky.

   | kite |
   |------|
   | tiny |
   | sky |

Name _____ Date _____

## /ō/ Sound and Spellings

**Focus** • The /ō/ sound can be spelled _ow, and oa_.

**Practice** Use the letters in parentheses ( ) to add to the spelling pattern given. Write the new word on the line. Letters in parentheses ( ) do not have to go in the order they are written.

**1.** (c, k, r)     __ __ o a __     _croak_

**2.** (l, e, b)     __ __ __ o w     _elbow_

**3.** (s, a, w, l, l)     __ __ __ __ __ o w     _swallow_

**4.** (t, r, h, t)     __ __ __ o a __     _throat_

**5.** (w, n, d, i)     __ __ __ __ o w     _window_

**Apply** Write a sentence with each word from above.
Possible answers below.

1. _I heard the toad croak._

2. _Andrew hit his elbow on the door._

3. _Did you swallow a fly?_

4. _My throat is sore this morning._

5. _Look out the window._

# /ō/ Sound and Spellings

**Focus** • The /ō/ sound can be spelled o and o_e.

**Practice** Circle the correct spelling for each word.

1. (cocoa)          coecoe

2. proetect      (protect)

3. hoep          (hope)

4. (cold)          coeld

5. (smoke)        smok

**Apply** Use the correct spelling of each word above in a sentence. Possible answers below.

1. I love to drink hot cocoa when it is snowing.

2. A mama bear will protect her cubs.

3. We hope pizza is for lunch today.

4. May I have a cold drink?

5. Smoke was coming from the fire.

Phonics • *Skills Practice 1*

Name _____ Date _____

# Selection Vocabulary

**Focus**

**ingredients** *n.* Plural of **ingredient**: a part that goes into a mixture.

**culture** *n.* The customs and beliefs of a group of people.

**dough** *n.* A mixture of flour, liquid, and other things that is usually baked.

**jalapeño** *n.* A small, hot pepper.

**international** *adj.* Having to do with two or more nations.

**Practice**  **Complete the crossword puzzle.**

**Across**

1. Having to do with two or more nations

4. The customs and beliefs of a group of people

5. A small hot pepper

**Down**

2. Parts that go in a mixture

3. A mixture of flour, liquid, and other things that is usually baked

**Apply** **Use your knowledge of the vocabulary words to complete the following activities.**
Possible answers below.

**1.** Write an example of a food that is made from *dough*.

bread

**2.** Write another word that could be used in place of the word *jalapeño*.

pepper

**3.** Write one example of a custom from your family's *culture*.

I get a piñata for my birthday every year.

**Write a sentence with each vocabulary word.**
Possible answers below.

| ingredients | dough | international | culture | jalapeño |
|---|---|---|---|---|

**1.** We need these ingredients to make bread.

**2.** Roll the dough into a big ball.

**3.** Our school has an International Day.

**4.** It is fun to learn about another culture.

**5.** The jalapeño tastes hot.

Name _____ Date _____

# Fact and Opinion

**Focus**
- A **fact** is a statement that can be proven true.
- An **opinion** is what someone feels or believes is true. Opinions cannot be proven true or false.

**Practice** **Look at the statements from "Jalapeño Bagels". In the spaces next to each statement, write *fact* if the statement is a fact. Write *opinion* if the statement is an opinion.**

1. Jam is better than lox. _____ opinion _____

2. Chocolate bars are the best dessert. _____ opinion _____

3. Pan dulce is a Mexican sweet bread. _____ fact _____

4. My father uses my grandmother's recipe to make the bagels.
   _____ fact _____

5. The Jewish braided bread is too beautiful to eat.
   _____ opinion _____

6. My teacher told us to bring something to school from our
   culture. _____ fact _____

**Apply** **Add a fact and an opinion to each sentence below. Use the clues in parentheses ( ).**

Possible answers below.

1. (opinion) Babies like to _sleep all day_____.

   (fact) Babies drink _milk_____.

2. (opinion) Globes are _fun to play with_____.

   (fact) A globe shows _land and water_____.

**Think about the story "Jalapeño Bagels". Write one sentence about food that is a fact and one that is an opinion.**

Possible answers below.

Opinion:

3. _Bagels are the best breakfast_
   _food._____

Fact:

4. _There are many different kinds of_
   _bread._____

Name _____ Date _____

# Explaining A Process

**Think** **Audience: Who** will read your paragraph?

_____

**Purpose: What** do you want your paragraph to do?

_____

**Prewriting** **Use the space below to plan a paragraph that gives directions for a recipe. Remember to put your steps in order.** Possible answers below.

**Recipe for:** Peanut Butter and Jelly Sandwich

**First**

Get out bread, peanut butter,

jelly, a butter knife, and a

plate.

**Second** Lay the bread on the plate

and open peanut butter and jelly

jars. Spread the peanut butter and

jelly on the bread with a butter knife.

**Then**

Put away the bread,

peanut butter, and jelly.

Wash the butter knife.

**Finally**

Eat the

sandwich.

## Revising    Use this checklist to revise.

- ☐ Do your sentences describe steps in the correct order?

- ☐ Did you use time and order words to sequence the steps?

- ☐ Are there details that need to be added to make the directions clear?

- ☐ Will your reader be able to follow the directions easily?

## Editing/Proofreading    Use this checklist to correct mistakes.

- ☐ Is your paragraph indented?

- ☐ Is every word or special term spelled correctly?

- ☐ Does every sentence start with a capital letter?

- ☐ Does every sentence end with correct punctuation?

## Publishing    Use this checklist to prepare for publication.

- ☐ Write or type a neat copy.

- ☐ Include a drawing or a map that shows the steps in the right order.

- ☐ Ask someone if they can follow your directions.

**Name** _____ **Date** _____

# Review: Long i and Long o Spellings

**Focus**
- Long vowels sound like their names.
- Long i can be spelled _igh, _y, _ie, i, and i_e.
- Long o can be spelled _ow, oa_, o, and o_e.

**Word List**
1. dry
2. tie
3. fight
4. why
5. tow
6. soap
7. below
8. bike
9. cone
10. oak

**Challenge Words**
11. July
12. twilight
13. shallow
14. cocoa
15. thigh

**Practice** **Sort the spelling words under the correct heading.**

long i spelled _igh

1. fight

long i spelled _ie

2. tie

long i spelled _y

3. dry

4. why

long i spelled i_e

5. bike

long o spelled _ow

6. tow

7. below

long o spelled oa_

8. soap

9. oak

long o spelled o_e

10. cone

**Apply** Rhyming Strategy Find the spelling word that rhymes with each pair of words below. The correct word will have the same spelling pattern as the pair of words.

1. bow     low      tow

2. hike    strike   bike

3. croak   soak     oak

4. light   night    fight

5. zone    phone    cone

Visualization Strategy Circle the correct spelling for each spelling word. Write the correct spelling on the line.

1. (dry)      drie       dry

2. bealoa    (below)    below

3. (why)     wie        why

4. tigh      (tie)      tie

5. (soap)    sope       soap

Name _____ Date _____

# Commas: Words in a Series

**Focus** • A **comma** is used after each item in a series or list of things except for the last one.

**Practice** **Commas have been left out in the sentences below. Put commas where they are needed in the lists.**

**1.** Fleas, flies, and bees drive me crazy!

**2.** Insects eat things such as wood, paper, and even other insects.

**3.** Bats, birds, and reptiles also eat insects.

**4.** What is red, juicy, and healthy? An apple!

**Find each sentence that has commas in the right place. Circle the letter in front of it.**

**1.** **a.** Cars can be red, blue, black, or green.

   **b.** Trees can be tall short, thin or wide.

**2.** **a.** The American flag is red, white, and blue.

   **b.** The Italian flag is red white, and green.

**Apply** **Write a list of items for each topic.** Possible answers below.

| Favorite Foods | Favorite Animals |
|---|---|
| 1. carrots | 1. dogs |
| 2. strawberries | 2. cats |
| 3. juice | 3. hamsters |

**Write a sentence for each topic, writing your list as a series of items using commas correctly.** Possible answers below.

1. My favorite foods are carrots, strawberries, and juice.

2. I think dogs, cats, and hamsters are the best pets.

**Read the story and add commas where they are needed. Use proofreading marks.**

Flowers have soft petals∧pretty colors∧and a nice smell. To grow flowers you must plant the seeds∧water the plants∧and pull the weeds. Flowers look pretty in a garden∧in your office∧or in your house. Today, we will plant purple pansies∧white daisies∧and lilies all around the border of the garden.

Name _____ Date _____

# /ū/ Sound and Spellings

**Focus** • The /ū/ sound can be spelled _ew and _ue.

**Practice** Read the following words aloud.

| cue | argue | nephew | rescue | review | pew |
|-----|-------|--------|--------|--------|-----|

**Write the words with the /ū/ sound spelled like *hue*.**

1. argue

2. rescue

3. cue

**Write the words with the /ū/ sound spelled like *few*.**

1. nephew

2. review

3. pew

**Underline the _ue or _ew spelling pattern. Change the first letter of the word to make a rhyming word with the same spelling pattern. Write the new word on the line.**

1. hue    cue

2. few    pew

 **Apply**  **Choose a word from the box to complete each sentence.**

| statue | barbecue | nephew | review | argue |
|---|---|---|---|---|
| few | value | view | curfew | rescue |

1. Alice has a niece and a ___nephew___.

2. What will we eat at the ___barbecue___?

3. There were only a ___few___ people at the store.

4. My sister and I sometimes ___argue___ over toys.

5. The ___value___ of friendship is priceless.

6. What a beautiful ___view___ of the forest!

7. Mr. Williams will ___review___ the spelling words.

8. Stand as still as a ___statue___.

9. A firefighter will ___rescue___ the kitten.

10. My ___curfew___ is nine o'clock tonight.

Name _____ Date _____

# /ū/ Sound and Spellings

**Focus** • The /ū/ sound can be spelled *u* and *u_e*.

**Practice** Read the following words aloud.

| humor | museum | cube | used | unit | amuse |

**Write the words with the /ū/ sound spelled like *human*.**

1. _____humor_____    3. _____unit_____

2. _____museum_____

**Write the words with the /ū/ sound spelled like *huge*.**

1. _____cube_____    3. _____amuse_____

2. _____used_____

**Use one word with the *u* spelling pattern and one word with the *u_e* spelling pattern from above to complete the sentence.**

His sense of _____humor_____ did not _____amuse_____ me.

**Apply** Circle the word in the sentence with the /ū/ sound. Write the word and the spelling pattern used on the blank lines.

**1.** Paula is allowed to play a game on the (computer.)

computer     u

**2.** Adam (refused) to eat his broccoli.

refused     u_e

**3.** I can see the birds better by looking through my (binoculars.)

binoculars     u

**4.** The (menu) has a list of all the desserts.

menu     u

**5.** We had a party to give (tribute) to our teacher.

tribute     u_e

Name _____ Date _____

# Selection Vocabulary

**Focus**

**taxes** *n.* Plural of **tax**: money that people or businesses must pay to support the government.

**council** *n.* A group of people who make decisions for a larger group.

**cashier** *n.* A person in charge of paying out or receiving money.

**elect** *v.* To choose by voting.

**routes** *n.* Plural of **route**: a road or other course used for traveling.

**mayor** *n.* The person who is the head of a city or town government.

**Practice** Draw a line to match each word on the left to its definition on the right.

1. cashier

2. elect

3. taxes

4. mayor

5. routes

a. person who is head of a city or town government

b. road or other course used for traveling

c. to choose by voting

d. person in charge of paying or receiving money

e. money that people or businesses pay the government for its support

6. council — f. a group of people who make decisions for a larger group

**Apply** Tell whether the boldfaced definition that is given for the underlined word in each sentence below makes sense. Circle *Yes* or *No*.

1. Our class will <u>elect</u> a new student body president.
**choose by voting** ..................................................... Yes   No

2. The <u>mayor</u> gave me a key to the city.
**person who is the head of a city or
town government** ..................................................... Yes   No

3. Mom paid the <u>cashier</u> for our groceries.
**to choose by voting** ................................................ Yes   No

4. The <u>council</u> made a decision.
**group of people who make decisions
for a larger group** ................................................... Yes   No

5. Everyone must pay <u>taxes</u>.
**a road or other course used for traveling** .............. Yes   No

6. Which <u>route</u> is the best way to get to school?
**a road or other course used
for traveling** .......................................................... Yes   No

Name _____ Date _____

# Drawing Conclusions

**Focus**
• Readers get ideas, or **draw conclusions**, about what is happening in a story by using clues from the story.

**Practice**
**Read the sentences below. Then use the clues to draw a conclusion.** Possible answers below.

• The classes at the town's dance school are always full.

• Many people watch when the dance students perform.

• Most children in town say they want to study dance.

• The dance school is moving to a bigger building next year.

Conclusion: ___These people like to dance.___

• Tom buys food at the pet store once a week.

• The many cages need to be cleaned daily.

• He enjoys spending time playing with his animal friends.

• Tom always says, "The more the merrier!"

Conclusion: ___Tom has lots of pets.___

**Apply**   **Write three sentences that are clues for the following conclusion.** Possible answers below.

**Conclusion: It is raining outside.**

1. I put on my raincoat.

2. I almost forgot my umbrella.

3. I hope my homework papers don't get wet.

**Now, write your own conclusion sentence and three sentences that will give clues.** Possible answers below.

Conclusion: It is lunchtime at school.

1. Suddenly, my stomach begins to rumble.

2. I look at the clock.

3. My teacher says it's time to go to the cafeteria.

**Find a partner. Read the clues to your partner and write down their conclusion.**

Partner's Conclusion: It's time to eat lunch.

**Ask your partner which clue helped them the most. Write the clue below.**

When the teacher said it's time to go to lunch.

Name _____ Date _____

# Writing a Summary

**Audience: Who** will read your summary?

_____

**Purpose: What** is your reason for writing your summary?

_____

**Use the graphic organizer below to write notes for your summary.** Possible answers below.

**Title of Article:** Local Family Cleans Up Park

**Main Idea:** A family in our city worked with neighbors to fix up a park.

**Detail about the main idea:** The family and neighbors picked up trash and cleaned areas.

**Detail about the main idea:** They planted flowers and fixed all of the equipment.

**Detail about the main idea:** All of the neighborhood children can play at the new park.

## Revising  Use this checklist to revise.

- ☐ Did you choose an article related to the Unit theme?
- ☐ Did you tell the most important points of the article?
- ☐ Did you use your own words?
- ☐ Is there information that is not from the article?
- ☐ Will the reader understand the information?

## Editing/Proofreading  Use this checklist to correct mistakes.

- ☐ Make sure all of your sentences are complete.
- ☐ Is every word or special term spelled correctly?
- ☐ Does every sentence start with a capital letter and end with correct punctuation?

## Publishing  Use this checklist to prepare for publication.

- ☐ Write or type a neat copy.
- ☐ Attach the article you summarized.

**Name** _____ **Date** _____

# Long u spelled _ew, _ue, u, and u_e

**Focus**
- Long vowels sound like their names.
- Some ways long u can be spelled are _ew, _ue, u, and u_e.

**Practice**  **Sort the spelling words under the correct heading.**

long u spelled _ew          long u spelled u

1. few                      7. music

2. mew                      8. human

long u spelled _ue          long u spelled u_e

3. cue                      9. pure

4. hue                      10. cute

5. rescue

6. value

**Word List**

1. cue
2. hue
3. few
4. music
5. pure
6. value
7. mew
8. cute
9. human
10. rescue

**Challenge Words**

11. fury
12. confuse
13. view
14. skew
15. argue

**Apply** Visualization Strategy Circle the correct spelling for each spelling word. Write the correct spelling on the line.

1. myoosic (music)          music

2. (cute)          kute          cute

3. reskew          (rescue)          rescue

4. (cue)          kew          cue

5. (mew)          mue          mew

**Proofreading Strategy Circle the misspelled words. Write the words correctly on the lines below.**

Every (yoomun) has a special (valew). However, very (fyoo) are quite as special as my grandpa. His smile is like (pewr) sunshine. It brings a bright, golden (hyue) to the entire room. When I feel gloomy, it is so nice to have my grandpa around to cheer me up!

1. human

2. value

3. few

4. pure

5. hue

Name _____ Date _____

# Subject/Verb Agreement

**Focus**
- A sentence has a **subject** and a **verb** that *agree*. This means that the subject and verb must both be singular, or they must both be plural.
- If the subject of a sentence is singular, the verb must be singular.
- If the subject of a sentence is plural, the verb must be plural.

**Practice**
Write *S* if the sentence has a singular subject and verb. Write *P* if the sentence has a plural subject and verb.

**1.** Many plants can be kept inside to grow.  _____P_____

**2.** Herbs are plants used in cooking.  _____P_____

**3.** A wildflower grows by itself outside.  _____S_____

**4.** An evergreen tree keeps its leaves all year long.  _____S_____

**Apply** **Write *am*, *is*, or *are* to agree with the subject in each sentence.**

**1.** We _____ are _____ learning about plants and trees.

**2.** A tree _____ is _____ a wooded plant.

**3.** I _____ am _____ enjoying these lessons.

**Write *have* or *has* to agree with the subject in each sentence.**

**1.** Evergreens _____ have _____ leaves or needles.

**2.** The desert _____ has _____ many plants.

**Read the following sentences. Choose the verb in parentheses ( ) that correctly completes each sentence.**

**1.** Bobby _____ rakes _____ the leaves in our yard when
(rake, rakes)
it is autumn.

**2.** The leaves _____ change _____ from green to brown,
(changes, change)
yellow, and orange.

**3.** We _____ have _____ a great time jumping in piles of leaves.
(have, has)

Name _____    Date _____

# Open and Closed Syllables

**Focus**

- An **open syllable** occurs when a syllable ends in a vowel. The vowel sound in an open syllable is usually long.

Example

   di • ner     se • cret

- A **closed syllable** occurs when a vowel is followed by a consonant and the vowel usually has a short sound.

Example

   win • ter     bet • ter

**Practice**   **Look at how the syllables are divided in the following words. Write open or closed to describe the syllables.**

**1.** better    bet   ter    _closed_

**2.** beside    be   side    _open_

**3.** faster    fast   er    _closed_

**4.** rewind    re   wind    _open_

**5.** motion    mo   tion    _open_

 **Divide the following words into syllables. Then write open or closed to describe the syllables.**

**1.** table ___ta___ ___ble___  ___open___

**2.** running ___run___ ___ning___  ___closed___

**3.** summer ___sum___ ___mer___  ___closed___

**4.** remote ___re___ ___mote___  ___open___

**Write the following words under the heading of "open" or "closed" to describe the syllables.**

| winner | blanket | behind | token |
|--------|---------|--------|-------|
| paper | chosen | letter | forget |

*Open Syllables*

**1.** ___paper___

**2.** ___chosen___

**3.** ___behind___

**4.** ___token___

*Closed Syllables*

**1.** ___winner___

**2.** ___blanket___

**3.** ___letter___

**4.** ___forget___

Name _____ Date _____

# /ū/ Sound and Spellings

**Focus** • The /ū/ sound can be spelled _ew and _ue.

**Practice** Write *ew* or *ue* on the blank line to complete the word. Write the word.

1. resc___ue___ ___rescue___
2. curf___ew___ ___curfew___
3. neph___ew___ ___nephew___
4. contin___ue___ ___continue___

**Apply** Use a word from above to complete each sentence.

1. Did you ___rescue___ my toy from the trash can?
2. What time is your ___curfew___?
3. I am my uncle and aunt's ___nephew___.
4. Should we ___continue___ reading the story?

Name _____  Date _____

# /ū/ Sound and Spellings

**Focus** • The /ū/ sound can be spelled *u* and *u_e*.

**Practice** Add the letters in parentheses ( ) to the spelling pattern given to make a word. Write the word on the line. The letters in parentheses ( ) do not have to go in the order given.

1. (n, t, i)      u __ __ __      _unit_

2. (h ,d, m, i)   __ u __ __ __   _humid_

3. (t, c)        __ u __ e       _cute_

4. (f, s )       __ u __ e       _fuse_

**Apply** Use a word from above to complete each sentence.

1. It is a hot and _____humid_____ day outside.

2. My new puppy is so _____cute_____.

3. Did a _____fuse_____ blow?

4. Our science _____unit_____ is about outer space.

Name _____ Date _____

## Selection Vocabulary

**Focus**

**aisles** *n.* Plural of **aisle**: the space between two rows or sections of something.

**sharp** *adj.* Exact.

**construction** *v.* The act of building something.

**arrangement** *n.* A plan.

**huddled** *v.* Past tense of **huddle**: to crowd together.

**tingle** *v.* To have a slight stinging feeling.

**Practice** Write the vocabulary word that matches each definition below.

1. arrangement    a plan

2. construction    the act of building something

3. sharp    exact

4. huddled    crowded together

5. tingle    to have a slight stinging feeling

6. aisles    spaces between two rows or sections of something

**Apply**  Circle the correct word that completes the sentence.

1. There were trucks and workers on the _____ site.
   **a. construction**   **b.** aisles   **c.** tingle

2. Different foods filled the _____ of the grocery store.
   **a.** sharp   **b. aisles**   **c.** arrangement

3. We _____ together to stay warm.
   **a.** aisles   **b.** sharp   **c. huddled**

4. Jessica and Abby have an _____ to share books.
   **a. arrangement**   **b.** huddled   **c.** tingle

5. Dinner will be at five o'clock _____!
   **a.** tingle   **b.** aisle   **c. sharp**

6. When I was sitting on the floor, my foot began to _____.
   **a.** huddled   **b. tingle**   **c.** sharp

Name _____  Date _____

# Writing a Persuasive Paragraph

**Think**   **Audience: Who** will read your persuasive paragraph?

_____

**Purpose: What** is your reason for writing a persuasive paragraph?

_____

  Use the graphic organizer to help you make your outline for a persuasive paragraph.

Possible answers below.

**I. Topic:** Two Recess Periods

  **A. Main Heading:** Students at our school should have two different recess periods instead of just one.

   **1. Supporting Reason:** Extra exercise is good for your body.

   **2. Supporting Reason:** Playing together helps you work better together on projects.

   **3. Supporting Reason:** Students will be ready to learn after burning off some energy.

## Revising · Use this checklist to revise.

- ☐ Does your paragraph begin with a topic sentence?
- ☐ Is your purpose clear?
- ☐ Do you persuade others to think a certain way?
- ☐ Do you have good reasons that support your opinion?
- ☐ Are there facts or details that need to be added?

## Editing/Proofreading · Use this checklist to correct mistakes.

- ☐ Is your paragraph indented?
- ☐ Is every word or special term spelled correctly?
- ☐ Does every sentence start with a capital letter?
- ☐ Does every sentence end with correct punctuation?

## Publishing · Use this checklist to prepare for publication.

- ☐ Write or type a neat copy.
- ☐ Read your paragraph one more time. Make sure all the parts are there.
- ☐ Create a poster about your topic that will persuade others.

Name _____ Date _____

# Open and Closed Syllables; Review Long u

**Focus**

- Long vowels sound like their names.

- Long u can be spelled _ew, _ue, u, and u_e.

- Open syllables end in a vowel sound. The vowel sound is usually long.

- Closed syllables end in a vowel followed by a consonant. The vowel sound is usually short.

**Word List**

1. open
2. humid
3. until
4. person
5. cancel
6. fuel
7. begin
8. wagon
9. number
10. minus

**Challenge Words**

11. continue
12. dial
13. united
14. radio
15. moment

**Practice** Find the spelling words that have the long u sound.

1. humid    2. fuel

Find two spelling words that have open syllables.

3. open    4. begin

Find two spelling words that have closed syllables.

5. until    6. person

**Apply** Proofreading Strategy Circle the spelling mistakes in the story below. Then write the misspelled words correctly on the lines.

Each (pursin) in our class will take a big math test today. We will (begen) at ten o'clock sharp. First, we will have to (numbor) our papers from one to ten. There will be questions like, "What is one hundred (mynes) thirty-nine?" and "What is six times seven?" Even though I studied hard, I am still nervous. I hope our teacher decides to (kansul) it!

7. person

8. begin

9. number

10. minus

11. cancel

**Meaning Strategy** Write in words to complete the sentences below. Choose from the following words: open, humid, until, fuel, wagon.

12. I was sweating because it was so **humid** outside.

13. You must remain seated **until** you finish your dinner.

14. In pioneer days, traveling by **wagon** was very common.

15. We need to **open** the window to let in some fresh air.

16. Let's make sure there is enough **fuel** in the car before we drive to Grandma's.

Name _____ Date _____

# Parts of a Book

**Focus** You can find all kinds of important information in books when you know where to look.

**Practice** **Pick one of your textbooks and use what you have learned about the parts of a book to find the following information.**

**1.** Title of book: _____

_____

**2.** Author: _____

_____

**3.** Copyright date: _____

_____

**4.** Does the table of contents show chapters, units, or story

titles? _____

_____

How many are there? _____

Write the name of one and the page on which it begins.

_____

_____

**5.** Does your book have a glossary? _____

_____

If yes, what is the first word listed? _____

_____

**6.** Does your book have an index? _____

_____

If yes, on what page does it begin? _____

_____

**Name** _____ **Date** _____

# Contractions

- **Contractions** make writing sound more like a conversation. There are two kinds of contractions. A **contraction** can be formed by putting together a verb and the word *not*.

Examples

| | |
|---|---|
| are not—aren't | do not—don't |
| did not—didn't | has not—hasn't |
| was not—wasn't | could not—couldn't |

- A **contraction** may be formed by combining a pronoun and a verb.

Example
I am—I'm

Circle the correct contraction in each sentence below.

1. Greenland **isn't** **don't** a continent.

2. There **won't** **aren't** a lot of people living in Greenland.

3. Hawaii **wasn't** **weren't** a state until 1959.

**Apply** Write the contraction for the boldfaced words in each sentence below.

1. **I am** going to Arizona in April.   _____ I'm

2. **I have** never been to the Southwest.   _____ I've

3. **I will** send you a postcard of the desert.   _____ I'll

4. **She is** my best friend.   _____ She's

5. I know **he is** coming to visit today.   _____ he's

## Add apostrophes where needed to make contractions. Use proofreading marks.

I couldn't think of anything to write. We're supposed to write a poem for class. It doesn't have to be a long poem. I can't think tonight! Couldn't I write about my life? I could, if it weren't so late.

## Write the contraction for the following words.

1. should not   shouldn't   3. have not   haven't

2. he is   he's   4. there is   there's

Grammar • *Skills Practice 1*

**Name** _____ **Date** _____

# Proofreading Marks

¶    Indent

¶ Once upon a time, many years ago, there lived a dinosaur named Rocky. He lived . . .

∧    Add something.

_shiny_
a∧penny

⌿    Take out something.

Rabbits live in i⌿n burrows.

≡    Make a capital letter.

c̲alifornia
≡

/    Make a small letter.

We go camping in S̸ummer.

sp⃝    Check spelling.

sp
⟨freind⟩

⊙    Add a period.

There are eight planets in the solar system ⊙